Illustrative Mathematics®

LEARN MATH FOR LIFE

GEOMETRY

Units

1 | 2

STUDENT WORKBOOK

Book 1

KendallHunt |

ISBN 978-1-5249-9132-6

AGA1.0

20211204

Evidence and Proof

GEOMETRY

Unit

1

STUDENT WORKBOOK

Book 1

Kendall Hunt |

Lesson 1: Build It

- Let's use tools to create shapes precisely.

1.1: The Right Tool

1. Copy this figure using only a pencil and no other tools.

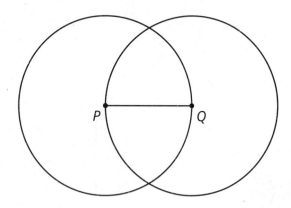

2. Familiarize yourself with your straightedge and compass by drawing a few **circles** of different sizes, a few **line segments** of different lengths, and extending some of those line segments in both directions.

iM KH

3. Complete these steps with a straightedge and compass:

   a. Draw a point and label it A.

   b. Draw a circle centered at point A with a radius of length PQ.

   c. Mark a point on the circle and label it B.

   d. Draw another circle centered at point B that goes through point A.

   e. Draw a line segment between points A and B.

1.2: Illegal Construction Moves

A   B

1. Create a circle centered at A with radius AB.

2. Estimate the midpoint of segment AB and label it C.

3. Create a circle centered at B with radius BC. This creates 2 intersection points. Label the one toward the top of the page as D and the one toward the bottom as E.

4. Use your straightedge to connect points A, D, and E to make triangle ADE and lightly shade it in with your pencil.

iM KH

1.3: Can You Make a Perfect Copy?

Here is a hexagon with all congruent angles and all congruent sides (called a *regular* hexagon).

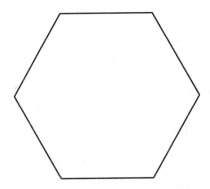

1. Draw a copy of the regular hexagon using only your pencil and no other tools. Trace your copy onto tracing paper. Try to fold it in half. What happened?

2. Here is a figure that shows the first few steps to constructing the regular hexagon. Use straightedge and compass moves to finish constructing the regular hexagon. Trace it onto tracing paper and confirm that when you fold it in half, the edges line up.

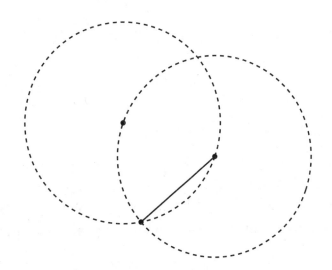

3. How do you know each of the sides of the shape are the same length? Show or explain your reasoning.

Are you ready for more?

Why does the construction end up where it started? That is, how do we know the central angles go exactly 360 degrees around?

Lesson 1 Summary

To construct geometric figures, we use a straightedge and a compass. These tools allow us to create precise drawings that someone else could copy exactly.

- We use the straightedge to draw a **line segment**, which is a set of points on a line with 2 endpoints.

- We name a segment by its endpoints. Here is segment AB, with endpoints A and B.

- We use the compass to draw a **circle**, which is the set of all points the same distance from the center.

- We describe a circle by naming its center and radius. Here is the circle centered at F with radius FG.

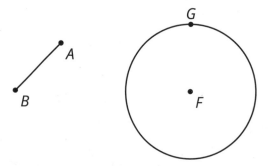

Early mathematicians noticed that certain properties of shapes were true regardless of how large or small they were. Constructions were used as a way to investigate what has to be true in geometry without referring to numbers or direct measurements.

Glossary

- circle
- line segment

iM KH

Lesson 1 Practice Problems

1. Here is a diagram of a straightedge and compass construction. C is the center of one circle, and B is the center of the other. Explain why the length of segment BD is the same as the length of segment AB.

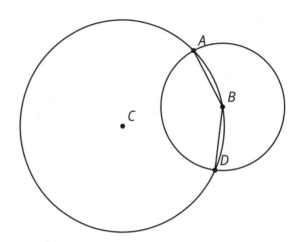

2. Clare used a compass to make a circle with radius the same length as segment AB. She labeled the center C. Which statement is true?

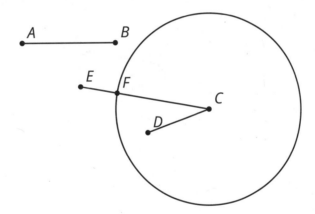

   A. $AB > CD$

   B. $AB = CD$

   C. $AB > CE$

   D. $AB = CE$

3. The diagram was constructed with straightedge and compass tools. Points A, B, C, D, and E are all on line segment CD. Name a line segment that is half the length of CD. Explain how you know.

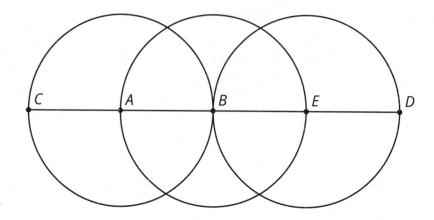

4. This diagram was constructed with straightedge and compass tools. A is the center of one circle, and C is the center of the other.

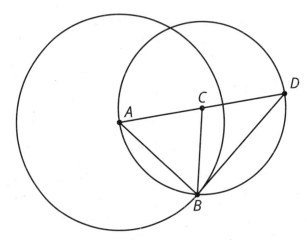

a. The 2 circles intersect at point B. Label the other intersection point E.

b. How does the length of segment CE compare to the length of segment AD?

iM KH

Lesson 2: Constructing Patterns

• Let's use compass and straightedge constructions to make patterns.

2.1: Math Talk: Why Is That True?

Here are 2 circles with centers A and B.

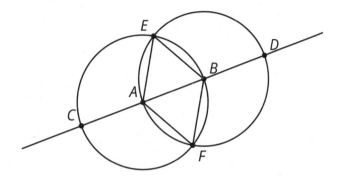

Based on the diagram, explain how you know each statement is true.

The length of segment EA is equal to the length of segment EB.

Triangle ABF is equilateral.

$AB = \frac{1}{3}CD$

$CB = DA$

2.2: Make Your Own

Use straightedge and compass moves to build your own pattern using the circle and radius as a place to start. As you make your pattern, record each move on a separate sheet of blank paper. Use precise vocabulary so someone can make a perfect copy without seeing the original. Include instructions about how to shade or color your pattern.

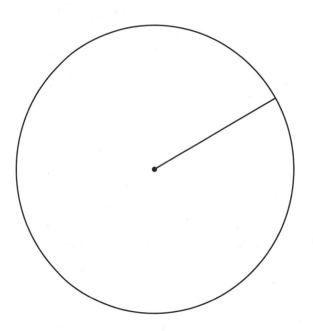

Are you ready for more?

If you have ever visited a mosque, madrasah, or other location where the religion of Islam is practiced, you may have noticed walls decorated with intricate geometric patterns. Throughout history, artists and craftspeople have developed these patterns which are based on compass and straightedge constructions.

You can find many tutorials online for creating these beautiful designs. Here is one example to try.

Video 'Fes Design' available here: https://player.vimeo.com/video/304121589.

2.3: Make Someone Else's

Follow the instructions precisely to recreate the pattern.

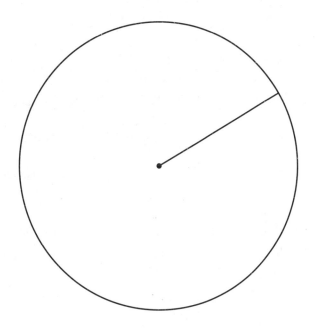

Lesson 2 Summary

We can use straightedge and compass moves to construct interesting patterns. What if someone else wants to make the same pattern? We need to communicate how to reproduce the pattern precisely. Compare these sets of instructions:

1. Start with a line and 2 points.

2. Create a line.

3. Create a circle.

4. Create a circle.

5. Create a circle.

6. Create a line.

---

1. Start with a line ℓ, point A on line ℓ and point B not on line ℓ.

2. Create a line through A and B extending in both directions. Label this line p.

3. Create a circle centered at A with radius AB. This circle intersects with line ℓ in 2 places. Label the intersection point to the right of A as C.

4. Create a circle centered at B with radius BA. This circle intersects with line p at A and 1 other point. Label the new intersection point as D.

5. Create a circle centered at D with a radius of length BC. This circle intersects with the circle centered at B in 2 places. Label the intersection point to the right of B as E.

6. Create a line through B and E extending in both directions.

It is important to label points and segments, such as point A or segment AB, to communicate precisely.

These are instructions to construct a line **parallel** to a given line. We say 2 lines are parallel if they don't intersect. We also say that 2 segments are parallel if they extend into parallel lines.

Glossary

- parallel

Lesson 2 Practice Problems

1. This diagram was created by starting with points A and B and using only straightedge and compass to construct the rest. All steps of the construction are visible. Describe precisely the straightedge and compass moves required to construct the line CD in this diagram.

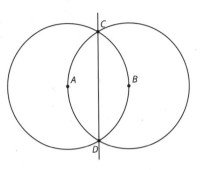

2. In the construction, A is the center of one circle, and B is the center of the other. Identify **all** segments that have the same length as segment AB.

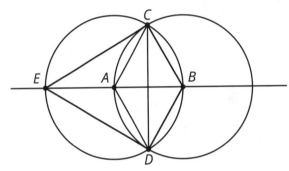

    A. segment AC

    B. segment AE

    C. segment BC

    D. segment CD

    E. segment DE

3. This diagram was constructed with straightedge and compass tools. A is the center of one circle, and C is the center of the other. Select **all** line segments that *must* have the same length as segment AB.

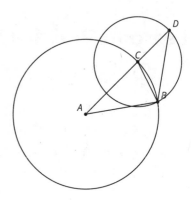

A. AB

B. AC

C. BC

D. BD

E. CD

(From Unit 1, Lesson 1.)

4. Clare used a compass to make a circle with radius the same length as segment AB. She labeled the center C. Which statement must be true?

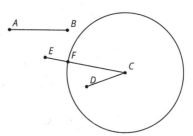

A. $AB = CD$

B. $AB = CE$

C. $AB = CF$

D. $AB = EF$

(From Unit 1, Lesson 1.)

iM KH

Lesson 3: Construction Techniques 1: Perpendicular Bisectors

- Let's explore equal distances.

3.1: Find All the Points!

Here are 2 points labeled A and B, and a line segment CD:

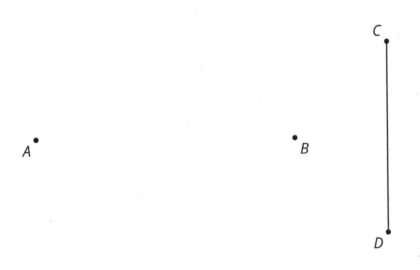

1. Mark 5 points that are a distance CD away from point A. How could you describe all points that are a distance CD away from point A?

2. Mark 5 points that are a distance CD away from point B. How could you describe all points that are a distance CD away from point B?

3. In a different color, mark all the points that are a distance CD away from both A and B at the same time.

3.2: Human Perpendicular Bisector

Your teacher will mark points A and B on the floor. Decide where to stand so you are the same distance from point A as you are from point B. Think of another place you could stand in case someone has already taken that spot.

After everyone sits down, draw a diagram of what happened.

Are you ready for more?

In this activity, we thought about the set of points on the floor—a two-dimensional plane—that were equidistant from two given points A and B. What would happen if we didn't confine ourselves to the floor? Start with two points A and B in three-dimensional space. What would the set of points equidistant from A and B look like?

3.3: How Well Can You Slice It?

Use the tools available to find the **perpendicular bisector** of segment PQ.

After coming up with a method, make a copy of segment PQ on tracing paper and look for another method to find its perpendicular bisector.

Lesson 3 Summary

A **perpendicular bisector** of a segment is a line through the midpoint of the segment that is perpendicular to it. Recall that a right angle is the angle made when we divide a straight angle into 2 congruent angles. Lines that intersect at right angles are called perpendicular.

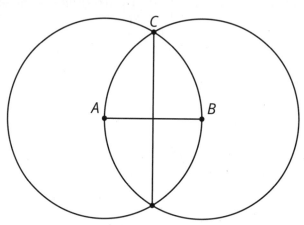

A **conjecture** is a guess that hasn't been proven yet. We conjectured that the perpendicular bisector of segment AB is the set of all points that are the same distance from A as they are from B. This turns out to be true. The perpendicular bisector of any segment can be constructed by finding points that are the same distance from the endpoints of the segment. Intersecting circles centered at each endpoint of the segment can be used to find points that are the same distance from each endpoint, because circles show all the points that are a given distance from their center point.

Glossary

- conjecture
- perpendicular bisector

Lesson 3 Practice Problems

1. This diagram is a straightedge and compass construction. A is the center of one circle, and B is the center of the other. Select **all** the true statements.

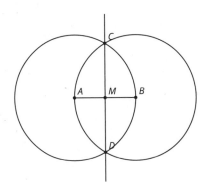

    A. Line CD is perpendicular to segment AB

    B. Point M is the midpoint of segment AB

    C. The length AB is the equal to the length CD.

    D. Segment AM is perpendicular to segment BM

    E. $CB + BD > CD$

2. In this diagram, line segment CD is the perpendicular bisector of line segment AB. Assume the conjecture that the set of points equidistant from A and B is the perpendicular bisector of AB is true. Is point E closer to point A, closer to point B, or the same distance between the points? Explain how you know.

$AB \perp CD$

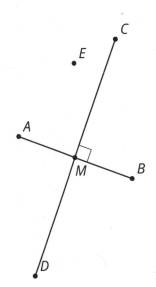

3. Starting with 2 marked points, *A* and *B*, precisely describe the straightedge and compass moves required to construct the triangle *ABC* in this diagram.

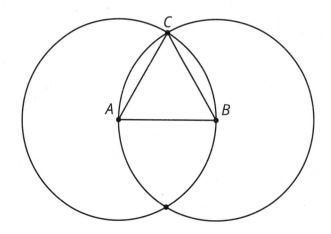

(From Unit 1, Lesson 2.)

4. This diagram was created by starting with points *C* and *D* and using only straightedge and compass to construct the rest. All steps of the construction are visible. Select **all** the steps needed to produce this diagram.

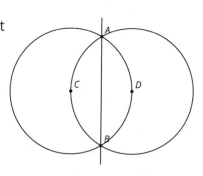

A. Construct a circle centered at *A*.

B. Construct a circle centered at *C*.

C. Construct a circle centered at *D*.

D. Label the intersection points of the circles *A* and *B*.

E. Draw the line through points *C* and *D*.

F. Draw the line through points *A* and *B*.

(From Unit 1, Lesson 2.)

iM KH

5. This diagram was constructed with straightedge and compass tools. A is the center of one circle, and C is the center of the other. Select **all** true statements.

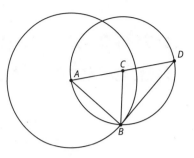

A. $AB = BC$

B. $AB = BD$

C. $AD = 2AC$

D. $BC = CD$

E. $BD = CD$

(From Unit 1, Lesson 1.)

Lesson 4: Construction Techniques 2: Equilateral Triangles

- Let's identify what shapes are possible within the construction of a regular hexagon.

4.1: Notice and Wonder: Circles Circles Circles

What do you notice? What do you wonder?

4.2: What Polygons Can You Find?

Here is a straightedge and compass construction of a regular hexagon **inscribed** in a circle just before the last step of drawing the sides:

1. Use a straightedge to draw at least 2 polygons on the figure. The vertices of your polygon should be intersection points in the figure. Lightly shade in your polygons using different colored pencils to make them easier to see.

2. Write at least 2 conjectures about the polygons you made.

4.3: Spot the Equilaterals

Use straightedge and compass moves to construct at least 2 equilateral triangles of different sizes.

Are you ready for more?

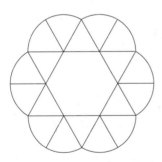
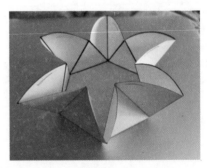

1. Examine the figure carefully. What different shapes is it composed of? Be specific.

2. Figure out how to construct the figure with a compass and straightedge.

3. Then, cut it out, and see if you can fold it up into a container like this.

Lesson 4 Summary

The straightedge allows us to construct lines and line segments, and the compass allows us to make circles with a specific radius. With these tools, we can reason about distances to explain why certain shapes have certain properties. For example, when we construct a regular hexagon using circles of the same radius, we know all the sides have the same length because all the circles are the same size. The hexagon is called **inscribed** because it fits inside the circle and every vertex of the hexagon is on the circle.

Similarly, we could use the same construction to make an inscribed triangle. If we connect every *other* point around the center circle, it forms an equilateral triangle. We can conjecture that this triangle has 3 congruent sides and 3 congruent angles because the entire construction seems to stay exactly the same whenever it is rotated $\frac{1}{3}$ of a full turn around the center.

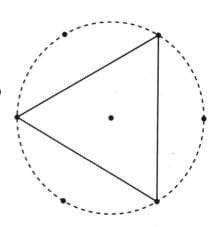

Glossary
- inscribed

Lesson 4 Practice Problems

1. This diagram is a straightedge and compass construction. A is the center of one circle, and B is the center of the other. Explain how we know triangle ABC is equilateral.

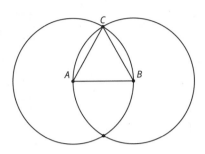

2. A, B, and C are the centers of the 3 circles. How many equilateral triangles are there in this diagram?

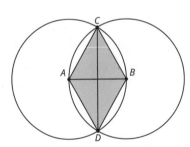

3. This diagram is a straightedge and compass construction. A is the center of one circle, and B is the center of the other. Select **all** the true statements.

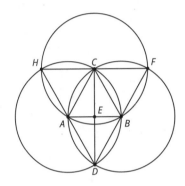

A. $AC = BC$

B. $AC = BD$

C. $CD = AB$

D. $ABCD$ is a square.

E. ABD is an equilateral triangle.

F. $CD = AB + AB$

4. Line segment CD is the perpendicular bisector of line segment AB. Is line segment AB the perpendicular bisector of line segment CD?

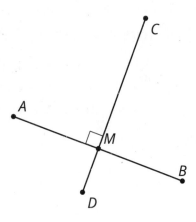

(From Unit 1, Lesson 3.)

5. Here are 2 points in the plane.

$\cdot\,A$ $\cdot\,B$

a. Using only a straightedge, can you find points in the plane that are the same distance from points A and B? Explain your reasoning.

b. Using only a compass, can you find points in the plane that are the same distance from points A and B? Explain your reasoning.

(From Unit 1, Lesson 3.)

iM KH

6. In this diagram, line segment CD is the perpendicular bisector of line segment AB. Assume the conjecture that the set of points equidistant from A and B is the perpendicular bisector of AB is true. Select **all** statements that must be true.

$AB \perp CD$

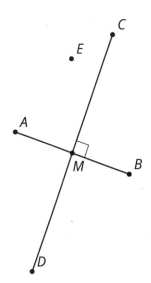

A. $AM = BM$

B. $CM = DM$

C. $EA = EM$

D. $EA < EB$

E. $AM < AB$

F. $AM > BM$

(From Unit 1, Lesson 3.)

7. The diagram was constructed with straightedge and compass tools. Name **all** segments that have the same length as segment AC.

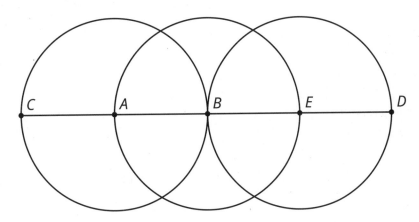

(From Unit 1, Lesson 1.)

8. Starting with 2 marked points, A and B, precisely describe the straightedge and compass moves required to construct the quadrilateral $ACBD$ in this diagram.

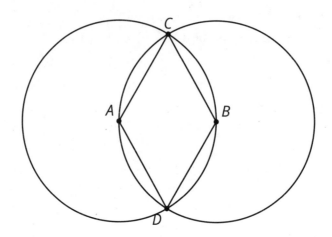

(From Unit 1, Lesson 2.)

9. In the construction, A is the center of one circle and B is the center of the other. Which segment has the same length as AB?

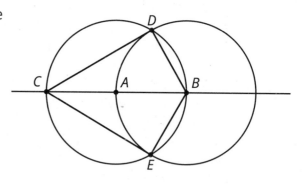

    A. CB

    B. CD

    C. CE

    D. CA

(From Unit 1, Lesson 2.)

iM KH

Lesson 5: Construction Techniques 3: Perpendicular Lines and Angle Bisectors

- Let's use tools to solve some construction challenges.

5.1: Two Circles

Points A and B are each at the centers of circles of radius AB.

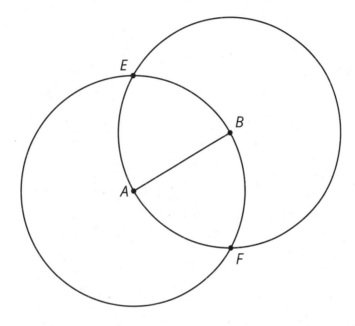

1. Compare the distance EA to the distance EB. Be prepared to explain your reasoning.

2. Compare the distance FA to the distance FB. Be prepared to explain your reasoning.

3. Draw line EF and write a conjecture about its relationship with segment AB.

5.2: Make It Right

Here is a line ℓ with a point labeled C. Use straightedge and compass moves to construct a line perpendicular to ℓ that goes through C.

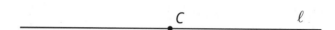

5.3: Bisect This

Here is an angle:

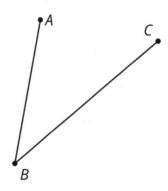

1. Estimate the location of a point D so that angle ABD is approximately congruent to angle CBD.

2. Use compass and straightedge moves to create a ray that divides angle CBA into 2 congruent angles. How close is the ray to going through your point D?

iM KH

3. Take turns with your partner, drawing and bisecting other angles.

    a. For each angle that you draw, explain to your partner how each straightedge and compass move helps you to bisect it.

    b. For each angle that your partner draws, listen carefully to their explanation. If you disagree, discuss your thinking and work to reach an agreement.

Are you ready for more?

For thousands of years since the ancient Greeks started playing with straightedge and compass constructions, people strived to find a construction to trisect an arbitrary angle into three equal angles. Many claimed to have found such a construction, but there was always some flaw in their reasoning. Finally, in 1837, Pierre Wantzel used a new field of mathematics to prove it was impossible—which still did not stop some from claiming to have found a construction. If we allow other tools besides just a straightedge and compass, though, it is possible. For example, try this method of using origami (paper folding) to trisect an angle.

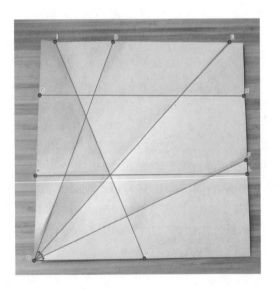

Video 'Trisecting an Angle with Origami' available here: https://player.vimeo.com/video/298418799.

Lesson 5 Summary

We can construct a line that is perpendicular to a given line. We can also bisect a given angle using only a straightedge and compass. The line that bisects an angle is called the **angle bisector**. Both constructions use 2 circles that go through each other's centers:

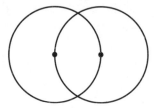

For the perpendicular line, start by finding 2 points on the line the same distance from the given point. Then create the 2 circles that go through each other's centers. Connect the intersection points of those circles to draw a perpendicular line.

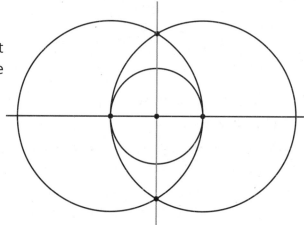

For the angle bisector, start by finding 2 points on the rays the same distance from the vertex. Then create the 2 circles that go through each other's centers. Connect the intersection points of those circles to draw the angle bisector.

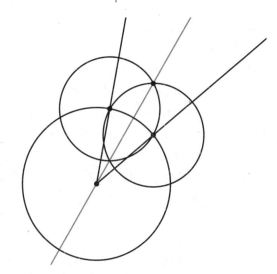

In fact, we can think of creating a perpendicular line as bisecting a 180 degree angle!

Glossary

- angle bisector

Lesson 5 Practice Problems

1. This diagram is a straightedge and compass construction of a line perpendicular to line AB passing through point C. Explain why it was helpful to construct points D and A to be the same distance from C.

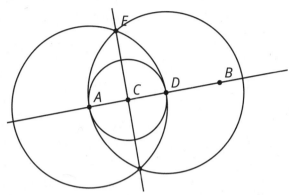

2. This diagram is a straightedge and compass construction.

   Select **all** true statements.

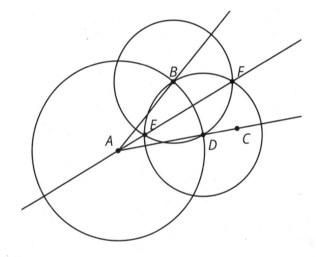

   A. Line EF is the bisector of angle BAC.

   B. Line EF is the perpendicular bisector of segment BA.

   C. Line EF is the perpendicular bisector of segment AC.

   D. Line EF is the perpendicular bisector of segment BD.

   E. Line EF is parallel to line CD.

3. This diagram is a straightedge and compass construction. A is the center of one circle, and B is the center of the other. A *rhombus* is a quadrilateral with 4 congruent sides. Explain why quadrilateral $ACBD$ is a rhombus.

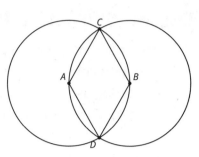

(From Unit 1, Lesson 4.)

4. A, B, and C are the centers of the three circles. Which line segment is congruent to HF?

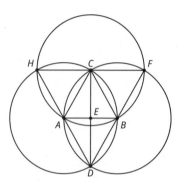

    A. AB

    B. CD

    C. DF

    D. CB

(From Unit 1, Lesson 4.)

5. In the construction, A is the center of one circle, and B is the center of the other. Explain why segment EA is the same length as segment BC.

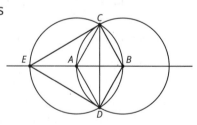

(From Unit 1, Lesson 2.)

iM KH

6. $AB \perp CD$

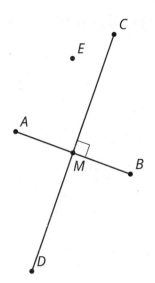

In this diagram, line segment CD is the perpendicular bisector of line segment AB. Assume the conjecture that the set of points equidistant from A and B is the perpendicular bisector of AB is true. Is point M closer to point A, closer to point B, or the same distance from both points? Explain how you know.

(From Unit 1, Lesson 3.)

7. A sheet of paper with points A and B is folded so that A and B match up with each other.

.A .B

Explain why the crease in the sheet of paper is the perpendicular bisector of segment AB. (Assume the conjecture that the set of points equidistant from A and B is the perpendicular bisector of segment AB is true.)

(From Unit 1, Lesson 3.)

8. Here is a diagram of a straightedge and compass construction. C is the center of one circle, and B is the center of the other. Explain why the length of segment CB is the same as the length of segment CD.

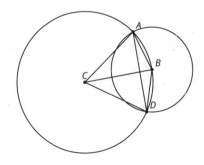

(From Unit 1, Lesson 1.)

Lesson 6: Construction Techniques 4: Parallel and Perpendicular Lines

- Let's use tools to draw parallel and perpendicular lines precisely.

6.1: Math Talk: Transformations

Each pair of shapes is congruent. Mentally identify a transformation or sequence of transformations that could take one shape to the other.

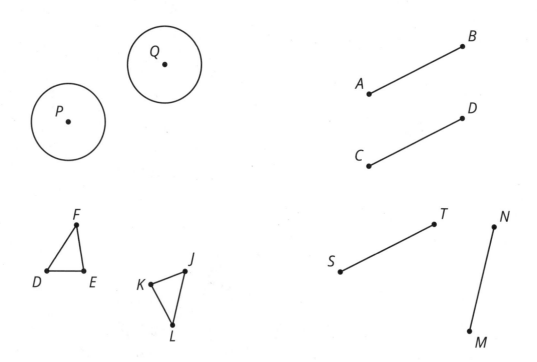

6.2: Standing on the Shoulders of Giants

Here is a line *m* and a point *C not* on the line. Use straightedge and compass moves to construct a line perpendicular to line *m* that goes through point *C*. Be prepared to share your reasoning.

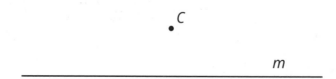

iM KH

Are you ready for more?

1. The line segment AB has a length of 1 unit. Construct its perpendicular bisector and draw the point where this line intersects our original segment AB. How far is this new point from A?

2. We now have 3 points drawn. Use a pair of points to construct a new perpendicular bisector that has not been drawn yet and label its intersection with segment AB. How far is this new point from A?

3. If you repeat this process of drawing new perpendicular bisectors and considering how far your point is from A, what can you say about all the distances?

6.3: Parallel Constructions Challenge

Here is a line m and a point C *not* on the line. Use straightedge and compass moves to construct a line parallel to line m that goes through point C.

Lesson 6 Summary

When we write the instructions for a construction, we can use a previous construction as one of the steps. We now know 2 new constructions that are made up of a sequence of moves.

- Perpendicular lines are lines that meet at a 90 degree angle.

- Parallel lines are lines that don't intersect. One way to make parallel lines is to draw 2 lines perpendicular to the same line.

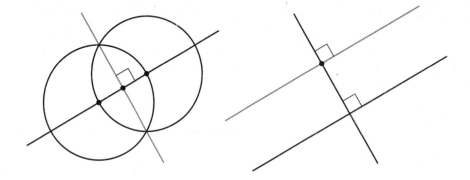

Lesson 6 Practice Problems

1. Which of the following constructions would help to construct a line passing through point C that is perpendicular to the line AB?

   A. Construction of an equilateral triangle with one side AB

   B. Construction of a hexagon with one side BC

   C. Construction of a perpendicular bisector through C

   D. Construction of a square with one side AB

2. Two distinct lines, ℓ and m, are each perpendicular to the same line n. Select **all** the true statements.

   A. Lines ℓ and m are perpendicular.

   B. Lines ℓ and n are perpendicular.

   C. Lines m and n are perpendicular.

   D. Lines ℓ and m are parallel.

   E. Lines ℓ and n are parallel.

   F. Lines m and n are parallel.

3. This diagram is a straightedge and compass construction of the bisector of angle BAC. Only angle BAC is given. Explain the steps of the construction in order. Include a step for each new circle, line, and point.

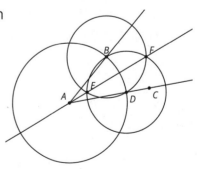

   (From Unit 1, Lesson 5.)

4. This diagram is a straightedge and compass construction of a line perpendicular to line AB passing through point C. Which segment has the same length as segment EA?

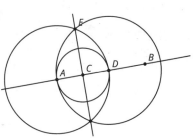

A. EC

B. ED

C. BE

D. BD

(From Unit 1, Lesson 5.)

5. This diagram is a straightedge and compass construction. Which triangle is equilateral? Explain how you know.

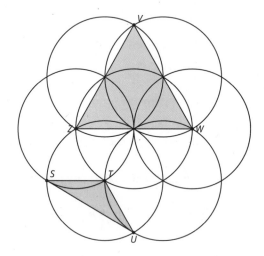

(From Unit 1, Lesson 4.)

6. In the construction, A is the center of one circle, and B is the center of the other. Name the segments in the diagram that have the same length as segment AB.

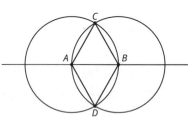

(From Unit 1, Lesson 2.)

7. This diagram is a straightedge and compass construction. A is the center of one circle, and B is the center of the other.

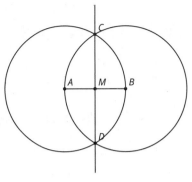

   a. Name a pair of perpendicular line segments.

   b. Name a pair of line segments with the same length.

(From Unit 1, Lesson 3.)

8. A, B, and C are the centers of the 3 circles. Select **all** the segments that are congruent to AB.

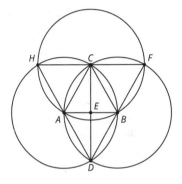

   A. HF

   B. HA

   C. CE

   D. CD

   E. BD

   F. BF

(From Unit 1, Lesson 4.)

Lesson 7: Construction Techniques 5: Squares

- Let's use straightedge and compass moves to construct squares.

7.1: Which One Doesn't Belong: Polygons

Which one doesn't belong?

A

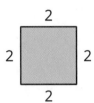

B

C

D

7.2: It's Cool to Be Square

Use straightedge and compass moves to construct a square with segment AB as one of the sides.

iM KH

7.3: Trying to Circle a Square

1. Here is square $ABCD$ with diagonal BD drawn:

    a. Construct a circle centered at A with radius AD.

    b. Construct a circle centered at C with radius CD.

    c. Draw the diagonal AC and write a conjecture about the relationship between the diagonals BD and AC.

    d. Label the intersection of the diagonals as point E and construct a circle centered at E with radius EB. How are the diagonals related to this circle?

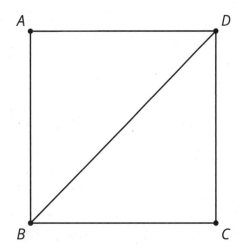

2. Use your conjecture and straightedge and compass moves to construct a square inscribed in a circle.

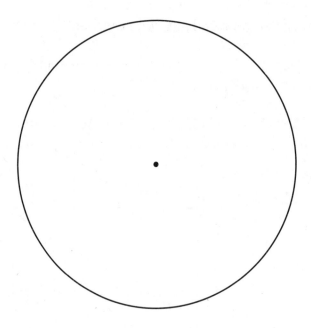

Are you ready for more?

Use straightedge and compass moves to construct a square that fits perfectly outside the circle, so that the circle is inscribed in the square. How do the areas of these 2 squares compare?

iM KH

Lesson 7 Summary

We can use what we know about perpendicular lines and congruent segments to construct many different objects. A square is made up of 4 congruent segments that create 4 right angles. A square is an example of a **regular polygon** since it is equilateral (all the sides are congruent) and equiangular (all the angles are congruent). Here are some regular polygons inscribed inside of circles:

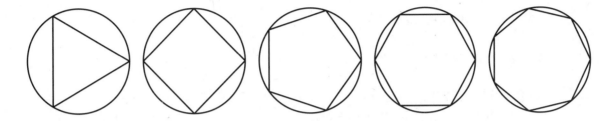

Glossary

- regular polygon

Lesson 7 Practice Problems

1. Which of these statements is true?

    A. All rectangles are regular polygons.

    B. All squares are regular polygons.

    C. All rhombi are regular polygons.

    D. All parallelograms are regular polygons.

2. This diagram is a straightedge and compass construction of a square $BACD$ (not all markings are shown). The construction followed these steps:

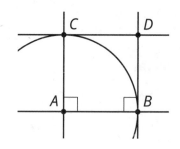

    a. Start with two marked points A and B

    b. Use a straightedge to construct line AB

    c. Use a previous construction to construct a line perpendicular to AB passing through A

    d. Use a previous construction to construct a line perpendicular to AB passing through B

    e. Use a compass to construct a circle centered at A passing through B

    f. Label an intersection point of that circle and the line from step 3 as C

    g. Use a previous construction to construct a line parallel to AB passing through C

    h. Label the intersection of that line and the line from step 4 as D

    i. Use a straightedge to construct the segments AC, CD, and DB

    Explain why you need to construct a circle in step 5.

iM KH

3. To construct a line passing through the point C that is parallel to the line AB, the first step is to create a line through C perpendicular to AB. What is the next step?

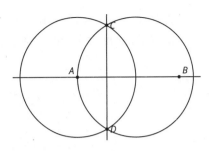

A. Construct an equilateral triangle with side CD.

B. Construct a line through point B perpendicular to AB.

C. Construct a segment with the same length as AB with endpoint C.

D. Construct a line through point C perpendicular to CD.

(From Unit 1, Lesson 6.)

4. Jada wanted to construct a line perpendicular to line ℓ through point C. The diagram shows her construction. What was her mistake?

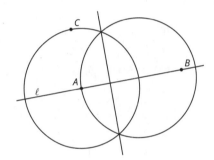

(From Unit 1, Lesson 6.)

5. Noah is trying to bisect angle BAC. He draws circles of the same radius with centers B and C and then uses one of the points of intersection for his ray. What mistake has Noah made in his construction?

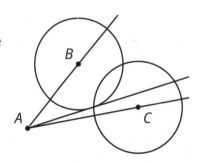

(From Unit 1, Lesson 5.)

6. Here is a straightedge and compass construction. Use a straightedge to draw an equilateral triangle on the figure. Explain how you know the triangle is equilateral.

(From Unit 1, Lesson 4.)

7. Here are 2 points in the plane. Explain how to construct a line segment that is half the length of segment AB.

•A •B

(From Unit 1, Lesson 3.)

iM KH

Lesson 8: Using Technology for Constructions

● Let's use technology to construct a diagram.

8.1: How Do Digital Construction Tools Work?

Open the Constructions App in the Math Tools (or at ggbm.at/C9acgzUx).

Try all the tools in the workspace.

1. Find the Undo button.

undo

2. Click on the image of 3 stacked segments, the Main Menu, to save your work or go to a new page.

main menu

3. Which tools do the same work as a straightedge?

4. The Constructions App has 3 tools to make a point. To learn about them, open the applet at ggbm.at/cuupdskk. In this applet, all 3 point tools have been used.
   a. Drag each point and each line around to see what happens in the Graphics View on the right.

   b. Look at the way the points are defined in the Algebra View on the left.

   c. Explain how each definition is related to the behavior of the corresponding point .

5. There are several ways to use the compass tool. First, set up a workspace that looks something like the image:

  a. Open a new blank page in the Constructions App.

  b. Draw circle A through point B.

  c. Draw segment CD not intersecting the circle centered at A.

  d. Draw point E not intersecting the circle centered at A or segment CD.

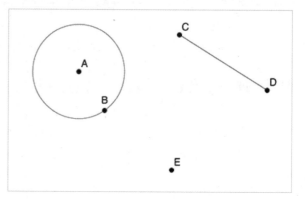

6. Select the compass tool and then click on segment CD. What happens?

7. Now click on the point E. What happens?

8. Make a new segment EF that is the same length as CD.

9. Make a circle with the same radius as the circle centered at A.

10. Explain how the digital compass tool is the same and how it is different from a physical compass.

8.2: Digital Compass and Straightedge Construction

Use the Constructions App in the Math Toolkit to create one or more of these figures:

- a perpendicular bisector of line segment AB

- an equilateral triangle

- a regular hexagon

- a square

- a square inscribed in a circle

- two congruent, right triangles that do not share a side

In order for your construction to be successful, it has to be impossible to mess it up by dragging a point. Make sure to test your constructions.

8.3: More Helpful Digital Tools

When you open the GeoGebra Geometry App geogebra.org/geometry, you'll see some basic tools. Click on the word "MORE" and you'll see some categories of tools, including "Construct" tools.

perpendicular line tool

parallel line tool

1. Construct a line or a line segment and an additional point that is not on it. Then try the perpendicular line tool and the parallel line tool. Use the move tool to drag some points around, and observe what happens.

2. Use any of the digital tools to create one or more of these figures. Test your constructions by dragging a point.

    a. parallelogram

    b. rectangle

    c. rhombus

    d. square

Lesson 8 Summary

We will start with a small set of tools. The GeoGebra Constructions App can be found at https://ggbm.at/C9acgzUx. These are the GeoGebra tools that do the same jobs as a pencil, a compass, and a straightedge.

Three pencil tools:

free point

point plotted on object

point of intersection of objects

Four straightedge tools:

line   **segment**   **ray**   **polygon**

Two compass tools:

circle with center through point   **compass**

The GeoGebra Geometry App is at https://www.geogebra.org/geometry. Click "MORE" to see the hidden categories of tools. Instead of doing each step of a construction, GeoGebra Geometry will perform all the steps of the constructions on our inventory. It has commands for perpendicular lines, parallel lines, and more!

perpendicular line tool   **parallel line tool**

Lesson 8 Practice Problems

1. Select **all** of the digital construction tools that do the same job as a pencil alone (without straightedge or compass).

    A. Point plotted on an object

    B. Polygon

    C. Circle with center through point

    D. Point of intersection

    E. Line

2. How can you test to see if a diagram made using digital tools is a construction or just a drawing based on estimation?

3. Han thought he constructed a rectangle using digital tools. When he moved point A the screen looked like this. What did Han do wrong?

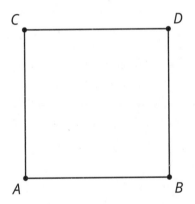 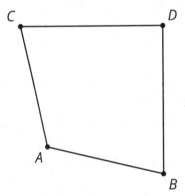

4. Select **all** the digital construction tools that do the same job as a straightedge.

    A. Circle with center through point

    B. Point plotted on an object

    C. Point of intersection

    D. Segment

    E. Line

5. Which digital construction tool does the same job as a compass?

    A. Point

    B. Line

    C. Polygon

    D. Circle with center through point

6. This diagram was made using digital construction tools. One of these triangles was made using the polygon tool and the other was made using the regular polygon tool. Explain what you could do to tell the difference between them.

7. Which digital construction tool would help you determine whether point C or point D is the midpoint of segment AB?

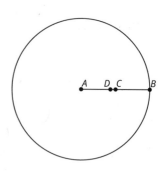

    A. Angle bisector

    B. Perpendicular bisector

    C. Perpendicular line

    D. Parallel line

iM KH

8. Here is as construction of a regular hexagon inscribed in a circle. Not all parts of the construction are shown. Explain how to construct an equilateral triangle inscribed in the circle centered at A using *digital construction tools*.

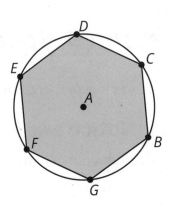

9. Here is a construction of a regular hexagon inscribed in a circle. Not all parts of the construction are shown. Explain how to construct a regular 12-sided polygon inscribed in the circle centered at A using *digital construction tools*.

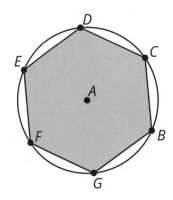

Lesson 9: Speedy Delivery

- Let's use perpendicular bisectors.

9.1: Notice and Wonder: Dots in a Square

What do you notice? What do you wonder?

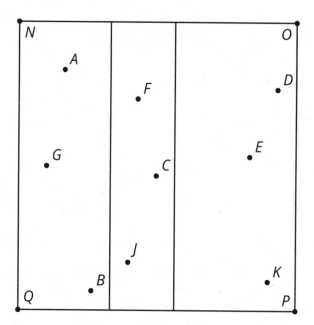

iM KH

9.2: Who Is Closest?

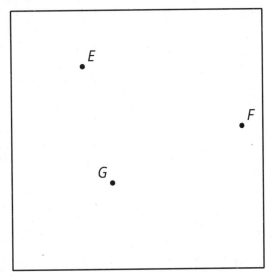

Here is a square city with 3 locations of the same store.

1. The company wants to break the city down into regions so that whenever someone orders from an address, their order is sent to the store closest to their home. They have hired you to decide how to partition the city between the 3 stores. Explain or show your reasoning.

2. If there are 100 employees, how should they be distributed among the 3 locations?

3. Is there anywhere in the city that has the same distance to all 3 stores?

4. Now a fourth store opens. Partition the city again.

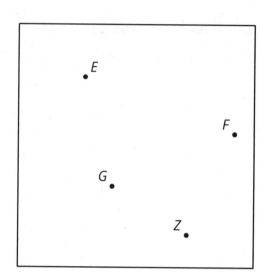

Are you ready for more?

In 1854, there was an outbreak of cholera in London. A physician named John Snow thought the water supply might be responsible. He made a map showing the location of all the water pumps in the city and the locations of all the deaths due to cholera in the city. How could he have used the ideas in this activity to help isolate the cause of the outbreak?

The diagrams you made in the activity and that Snow made are called Voronoi diagrams, and are still actively studied by mathematicians.

9.3: Now Who is Closest?

Use technology to explore the same type of problem from the earlier activity, "Who Is Closest?", with a larger number of points, such as all major airports in the U.S.

9.4: Another Layer

Your teacher will give you a **tessellation**.

1. Mark the intersection points on the tessellation.

2. Imagine that each point is a store from the "Who Is Closest?" activity. Repeat the process you used there to define the regions that are closest to each of the points.

3. Use color or shading to enhance your design.

Lesson 9 Summary

A **tessellation** is an arrangement of figures that covers the entire plane without gaps or overlaps. A simple example is a square grid. So that means graph paper is a tessellation. Here is another tessellation made of quadrilaterals. Can you see how repeating this pattern could cover the entire plane?

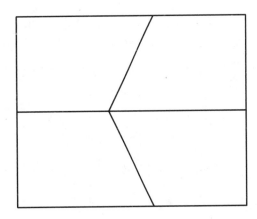

One way to draw a new tessellation is to decompose the plane into regions that are closest to each vertex. This method uses perpendicular bisectors and is called a Voronoi diagram. It is also a tessellation. What would this pattern look like when it is extended to cover the entire plane?

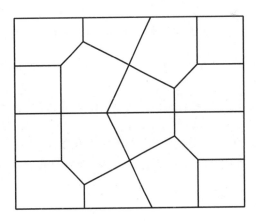

Glossary

- tessellation

Lesson 9 Practice Problems

1. Which construction can be used to determine whether point C is closer to point A or point B?

   A. Construct triangle ABC.

   B. Construct a line perpendicular to segment AB through point C.

   C. Construct the bisector of angle ACB.

   D. Construct the perpendicular bisector of segment AB.

2. The diagram is a straightedge and compass construction. Lines ℓ, m, and n are the perpendicular bisectors of the sides of triangle ABC. Select **all** the true statements.

   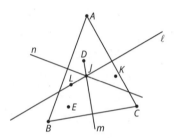

   A. Point E is closer to point A than it is to point C.

   B. Point L is closer to point B than it is to point A.

   C. Point D is closer to point B than it is to point C.

   D. Point J is closer to point A than it is to point B or point C.

   E. Point K is closer to point C than it is to point A or point B.

   F. Point L is closer to point C than it is to point A or point B.

3. Decompose the figure into regions that are closest to each vertex. Explain or show your reasoning.

   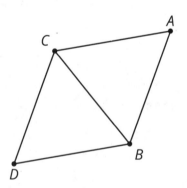

4. Which construction could be used to construct an isosceles triangle ABC given line segment AB?

    A. Mark a third point C not on segment AB. Draw segments AC and BC.

    B. Label a point C on segment AB and construct a line perpendicular to AB through point C. Draw segments AC and BC.

    C. Construct the perpendicular bisector of segment AB. Mark the intersection of this line and AB and label it C. Draw segments AC and BC.

    D. Construct the perpendicular bisector of segment AB. Mark any point C on the perpendicular bisector except where it intersects AB. Draw segments AC and BC.

5. Select **all** true statements about regular polygons.

    A. All angles are right angles.

    B. All angles are congruent.

    C. All side lengths are equal.

    D. There are exactly 4 sides.

    E. There are at least 3 sides.

(From Unit 1, Lesson 7.)

6. This diagram shows the beginning of a straightedge and compass construction of a rectangle.

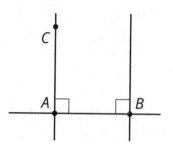

The construction followed these steps:

   a. Start with two marked points A and B

   b. Use a straightedge to construct line AB

   c. Use a previous construction to construct a line perpendicular to AB passing through A

   d. Use a previous construction to construct a line perpendicular to AB passing through B

   e. Mark a point C on the line perpendicular to AB passing through A

Explain the steps needed to complete this construction.

(From Unit 1, Lesson 7.)

7. This diagram is a straightedge and compass construction. Is it important that the circle with center B passes through D and that the circle with center D passes through B? Show or explain your reasoning.

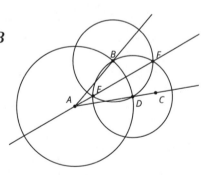

(From Unit 1, Lesson 5.)

iM KH

Lesson 10: Rigid Transformations

- Let's draw some transformations.

10.1: Notice and Wonder: Transformed

What do you notice? What do you wonder?

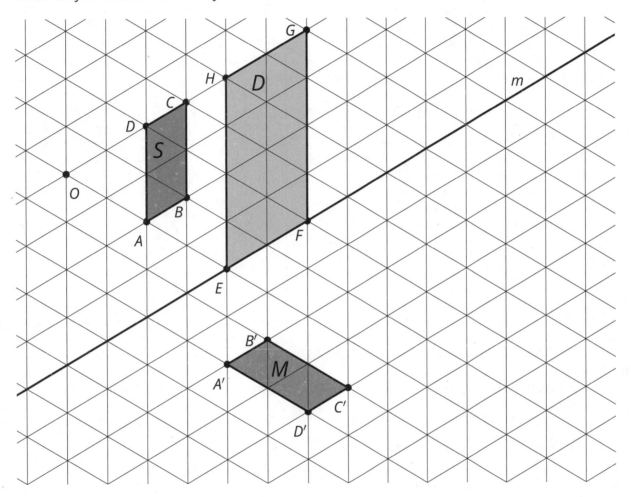

10.2: What's the Same?

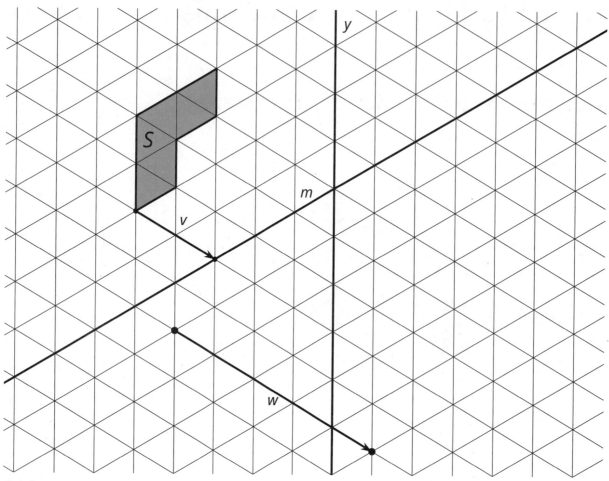

Draw each **rigid transformation** in a different color.

1. **Translate** figure S along the line segment v in the direction shown by the arrow.
   Color: _____

2. **Reflect** figure S across line y. Color: _____

3. Reflect figure S across line m. Color: _____

4. Translate figure S along the line segment w in the direction shown by the arrow.
   Reflect this **image** across line y. Color: _____

5. How are the images the same? How are they different?

iM KH

10.3: Does Order Matter?

Here are 3 **congruent** L shapes on a grid.

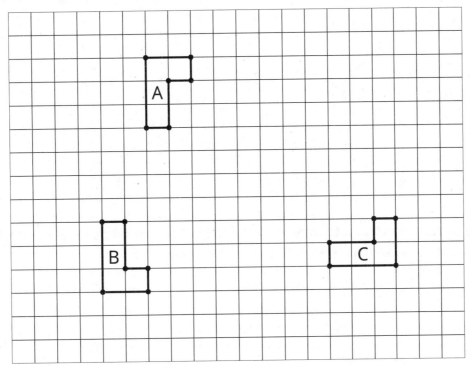

1. Describe a sequence of transformations that will take Figure A onto Figure B.

2. If you reverse the order of your sequence, will the reverse sequence still take A onto B?

3. Describe a sequence of transformations that will take Figure A onto Figure C.

4. If you reverse the order of your sequence, will the reverse sequence still take A onto C?

Are you ready for more?

1. Construct some examples of sequences of two rigid transformations that take Figure A to a new Figure D where reversing the order of the sequence also takes Figure A to Figure D.

2. Make some conjectures about when reversing the order of a sequence of two rigid transformations still takes a figure to the same place.

Lesson 10 Summary

A figure is called **congruent** to another figure if there is a sequence of translations, rotations, and reflections that takes one of the figures onto the other. This is because translations, rotations, and reflections are rigid motions. Any sequence of rigid motions is called a **rigid transformation**. A rigid transformation is a transformation that doesn't change measurements on any figure. With a rigid transformation, figures like polygons have corresponding sides of the same length and corresponding angles of the same measure.

The result of any transformation is called the **image**. The points in the original figure are the inputs for the transformation sequence and are named with capital letters. The points in the image are the outputs and are named with capital letters and an apostrophe, which is referred to as "prime."

There are many ways to show that 2 figures are congruent since many sequences of transformations take a figure to the same image. However, order matters in a set of

iM KH

instructions. Sometimes we can switch 2 steps in a sequence and get the same output, but other times, switching 2 steps results in a different image. These 2 sequences of transformations both have the points A, B, and C as inputs and points A'', B'', and C'' as outputs. Each step in the sequences of rigid transformations creates a triangle that is congruent to triangle ABC.

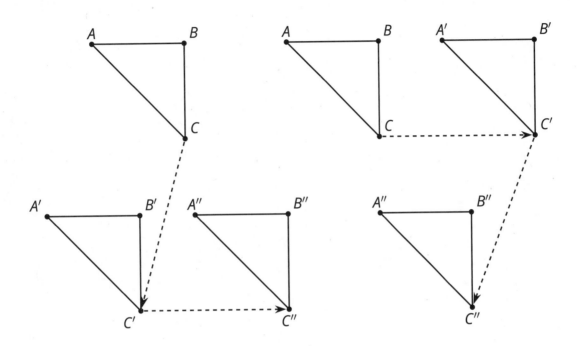

Glossary

- assertion
- congruent
- image
- rigid transformation
- theorem

Lesson 10 Practice Problems

1. Here are 4 triangles that have each been transformed by a different transformation. Which transformation is *not* a rigid transformation?

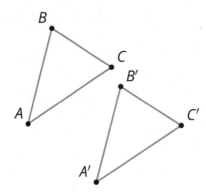

A.

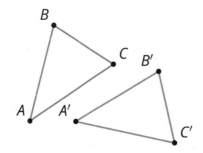

B.

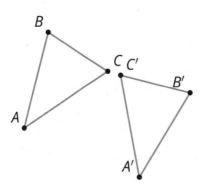

C.

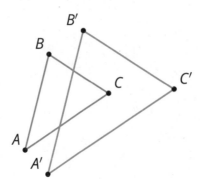

D.

iM KH

2. What is the definition of congruence?

   A. If two figures have the same shape, then they are congruent.

   B. If two figures have the same area, then they are congruent.

   C. If there is a sequence of transformations taking one figure to another, then they are congruent.

   D. If there is a sequence of rotations, reflections, and translations that take one figure to the other, then they are congruent.

3. There is a sequence of rigid transformations that takes A to A', B to B', and C to C'. The same sequence takes D to D'. Draw and label D':

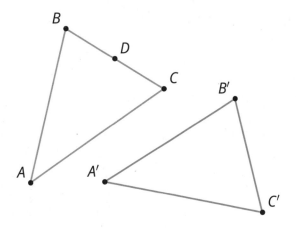

4. Three schools are located at points A, B, and C. The school district wants to locate its new stadium at a location that will be roughly the same distance from all 3 schools. Where should they build the stadium? Explain or show your reasoning.

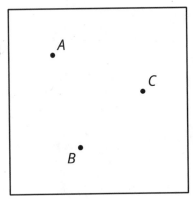

(From Unit 1, Lesson 9.)

5. To construct a line passing through point C that is parallel to the line AB, Han constructed the perpendicular bisector of AB and then drew line CD.

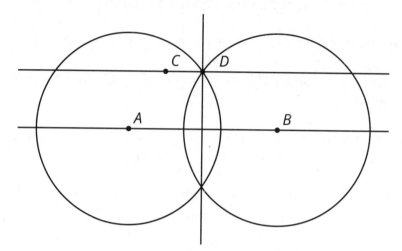

Is CD guaranteed to be parallel to AB? Explain how you know.

(From Unit 1, Lesson 6.)

6. This diagram is a straightedge and compass construction of a line perpendicular to line AB passing through point C. Select **all** the statements that must be true.

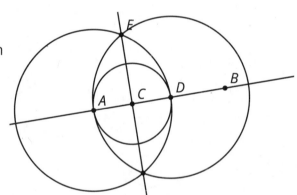

A. $AD = BD$

B. $EC = AD$

C. $AC = DC$

D. $EA = ED$

E. $ED = DB$

F. $CB = AD$

(From Unit 1, Lesson 5.)

iM KH

Lesson 11: Defining Reflections

- Let's reflect some figures.

11.1: Which One Doesn't Belong: Crossing the Line

Which one doesn't belong?

Figure 1

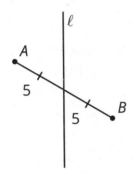

Figure 2

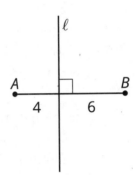

Figure 3

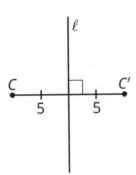

Figure 4

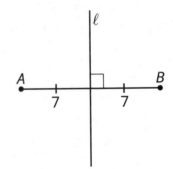

11.2: Info Gap: What's the Point: Reflections

Your teacher will give you either a problem card or a data card. Do not show or read your card to your partner.

If your teacher gives you the data card:

1. Silently read the information on your card.

2. Ask your partner "What specific information do you need?" and wait for your partner to ask for information. Only give information that is on your card. (Do not figure out anything for your partner!)

3. Before telling your partner the information, ask "Why do you need to know (that piece of information)?"

4. Read the problem card, and solve the problem independently.

5. Share the data card, and discuss your reasoning.

If your teacher gives you the problem card:

1. Silently read your card and think about what information you need to answer the question.

2. Ask your partner for the specific information that you need.

3. Explain to your partner how you are using the information to solve the problem.

4. When you have enough information, share the problem card with your partner, and solve the problem independently.

5. Read the data card, and discuss your reasoning.

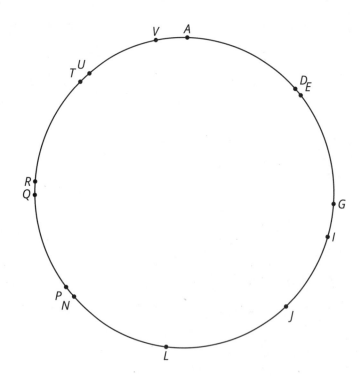

11.3: Triangle in the Mirror

Kiran started reflecting triangle CDE across line m. So far, he knows the image of D is D' and the image of E is E'.

1. Annotate Kiran's diagram to show how he reflected point D.

2. Use straightedge and compass moves to determine the location of C'. Then lightly shade in triangle $C'D'E'$.

3. Write a set of instructions for how to reflect any point P across a given line ℓ.

Kiran's Diagram

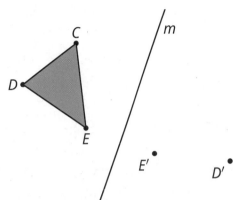

Elena's Diagram

4. Elena found C' incorrectly. Elena is convinced that triangle $C'D'E'$ "looks fine." Explain to Elena why her C' is not a reflection of point C across line m.

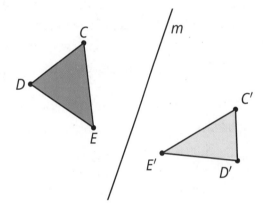

Are you ready for more?

1. Using your response from question 2 (with the correct location of C'):
    a. Draw the line CC'.

    b. Reflect triangle $C'D'E'$ across line CC'.

    c. Label the image $C''D''E''$.

2. Find a single rigid motion that takes CDE to $C''D''E''$.

Lesson 11 Summary

Think about reflecting the point A across line ℓ:

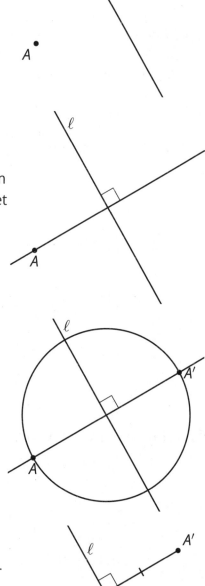

The image A' is somewhere on the other side of ℓ from A. The line ℓ is the boundary between all the points that are closer to A and all the points that are closer to A'. In other words, ℓ is the set of points that are the same distance from A as from A'. In a previous lesson, we conjectured that a set of points that are the same distance from A as from A' is the perpendicular bisector of the segment AA'. Using a construction technique from a previous lesson, we can construct a line perpendicular to ℓ that goes through A:

A' lies on this new line at the same distance from ℓ as A:

We define the **reflection** across line ℓ as a transformation that takes each point A to a point A' as follows: A' lies on the line through A that is perpendicular to ℓ, is on the other side of ℓ, and is the same distance from ℓ as A. If A happens to be on line ℓ, then A and A' are both at the same location (they are both a distance of zero from line ℓ).

Glossary

- reflection

Lesson 11 Practice Problems

1. Which of these constructions would construct a line of reflection that takes the point *A* to point *B*?

   A. Construct the perpendicular bisector of segment *AB*.

   B. Construct a line through *B* perpendicular to segment *AB*.

   C. Construct the line passing through *A* and *B*.

   D. Construct a line parallel to line *AB*.

2. A point *P* stays in the same location when it is reflected over line ℓ.

   What can you conclude about *P*?

3. Lines ℓ and *m* are perpendicular with point of intersection *P*.

   $m \perp \ell$

   Noah says that a 180 degree rotation, with center *P*, has the same effect on points in the plane as reflecting over line *m*. Do you agree with Noah? Explain your reasoning.

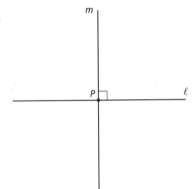

4. Here are 4 triangles that have each been transformed by a different transformation. Which transformation is *not* a rigid transformation?

A.
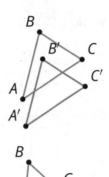

B.
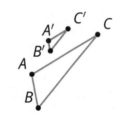

C.
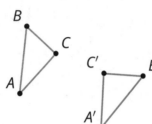

D.
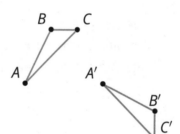

(From Unit 1, Lesson 10.)

5. There is a sequence of rigid transformations that takes A to A', B to B', and C to C'. The same sequence takes D to D'. Draw and label D':

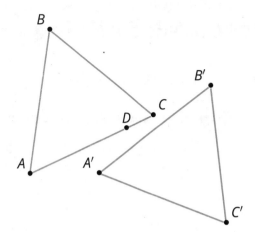

(From Unit 1, Lesson 10.)

6. Here are 3 points in the plane. Explain how to determine whether point C is closer to point A or point B.

•C

•A   •B

(From Unit 1, Lesson 9.)

7. Diego says a quadrilateral with 4 congruent sides is always a regular polygon. Mai say it never is one. Do you agree with either of them?

(From Unit 1, Lesson 7.)

Lesson 12: Defining Translations

- Let's translate some figures.

12.1: Notice and Wonder: Two Triangles and an Arrow

What do you notice? What do you wonder?

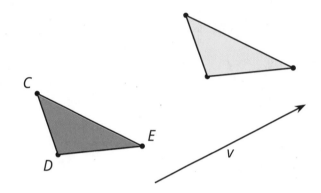

iM KH

12.2: What's the Point: Translations

1. After a translation, the image of V is W. Find at least 3 other points that are taken to a labeled point by that translation.

2. Write at least 1 conjecture about translations.

3. In a new translation, the image of V is Z. Find at least 3 other points that are taken to a labeled point by the new translation.

4. Are your conjectures still true for the new translation?

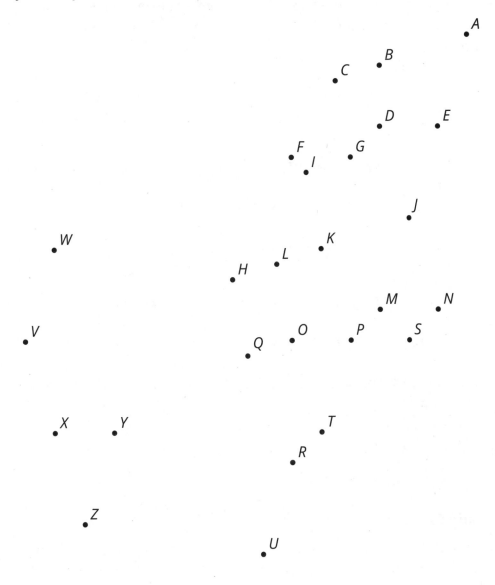

12.3: Translating Triangles

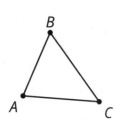

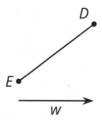

1. Translate triangle ABC by the **directed line segment** from A to C.
   a. What is the relationship between line BC and line $B'C'$? Explain your reasoning.

   b. How does the length of segment BC compare to the length of segment $B'C'$? Explain your reasoning.

2. Translate segment DE by directed line segment w. Label the new endpoints D' and E'.
   a. Connect D to D' and E to E'.

   b. What kind of shape did you draw? What properties does it have? Explain your reasoning.

Are you ready for more?

1. On triangle ABC in the task, use a straightedge and compass to construct the line which passes through A and is perpendicular to AC. Label it ℓ. Then, construct the perpendicular bisector of AC and label it m. Draw the reflection of ABC across the line ℓ. Since the label $A'B'C'$ is used already, label it DEF instead.

iM KH

2. What is the reflection of DEF across the line m?

3. Explain why this is cool.

Lesson 12 Summary

A translation slides a figure in a given direction for a given distance with no rotation. The distance and direction is given by a **directed line segment**. The arrow of the directed line segment specifies the direction of the translation, and the length of the directed line segment specifies how far the figure gets translated.

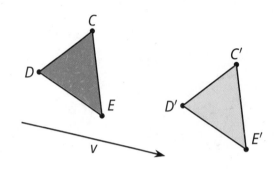

More precisely, a **translation** of a point A along a directed line segment t is a transformation that takes A to A' so that the directed line segment AA' is parallel to t, goes in the same direction as t, and is the same length as t.

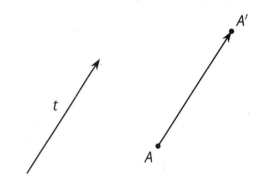

Here is a translation of 3 points. Notice that the directed line segments CC', DD', and EE' are each parallel to v, going in the same direction as v, and the same length as v.

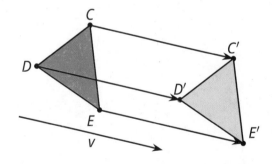

Glossary

- directed line segment
- translation

Lesson 12 Practice Problems

1. Match the directed line segment with the image of Polygon P being transformed to Polygon Q by translation by that directed line segment.

Translation 1   **Translation 2**

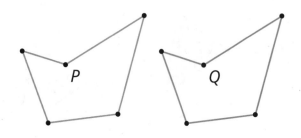

Translation 3   **Translation 4**

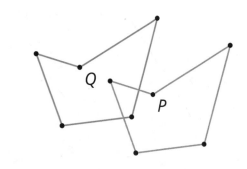

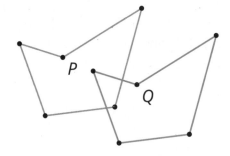

A.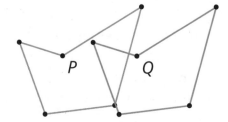

1. Translation 1

2. Translation 2

B.

3. Translation 3

C.

4. Translation 4

D.

iM KH

2. Draw the image of quadrilateral $ABCD$ when translated by the directed line segment v. Label the image of A as A', the image of B as B', the image of C as C' and the image of D as D'.

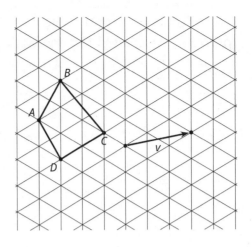

3. Which statement is true about a translation?

   A. A translation takes a line to a parallel line or itself.

   B. A translation takes a line to a perpendicular line.

   C. A translation requires a center of translation.

   D. A translation requires a line of translation.

4. Select **all** the points that stay in the same location after being reflected across line ℓ.

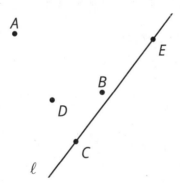

   A. A

   B. B

   C. C

   D. D

   E. E

(From Unit 1, Lesson 11.)

5. Lines ℓ and m are perpendicular. A point Q has this property: rotating Q 180 degrees using center P has the same effect as reflecting Q over line m.

$m \perp \ell$

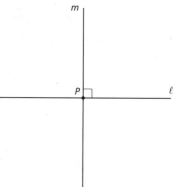

   a. Give two possible locations of Q.

   b. Do all points in the plane have this property?

(From Unit 1, Lesson 11.)

6. There is a sequence of rigid transformations that takes A to A', B to B', and C to C'. The same sequence takes D to D'. Draw and label D':

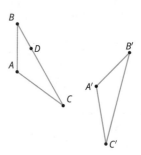

(From Unit 1, Lesson 10.)

7. Two distinct lines, ℓ and m, are each perpendicular to the same line n.

   a. What is the measure of the angle where line ℓ meets line n?

   b. What is the measure of the angle where line m meets line n?

(From Unit 1, Lesson 6.)

iM KH

Lesson 13: Incorporating Rotations

Let's draw some transformations.

13.1: Left to Right

The semaphore alphabet is a way to use flags to signal messages. Here's how to signal the letters Z and J. For each, precisely describe a rotation that would take the left hand flag to the right hand flag.

Z

J

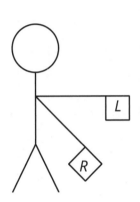 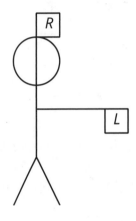

13.2: Turning on a Grid

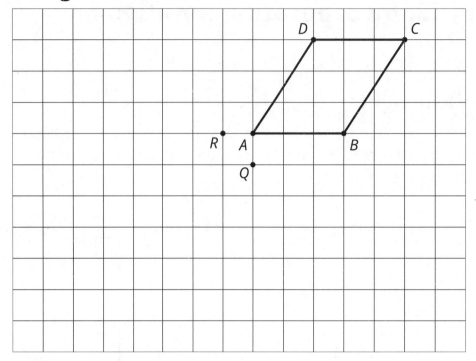

1. Rotate $ABCD$ 90 degrees clockwise around Q.

2. Rotate $ABCD$ 180 degrees around R.

3. Rotate $HJKLMN$ 120 degrees clockwise around O.

4. Rotate $HJKLMN$ 60 degrees counterclockwise around P.

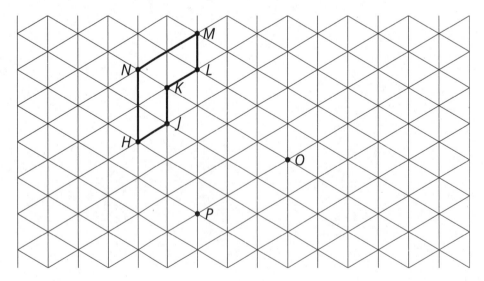

iM KH

13.3: Translate, Rotate, Reflect

Mai suspects triangle ABC is congruent to triangle DEF. She thinks these steps will work to show there is a rigid transformation from ABC to DEF.

- Translate by directed line segment v.

- Rotate the image ___ degrees clockwise around point D.

- Reflect that image over line DE.

Draw each image and determine the angle of rotation needed for these steps to take ABC to DEF.

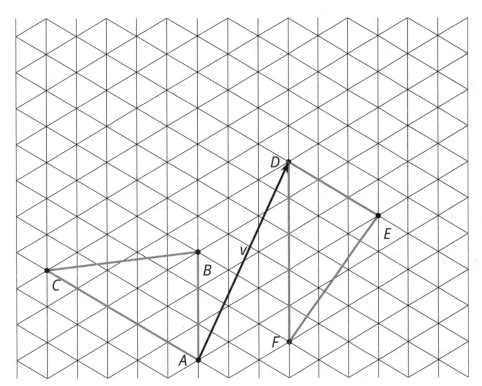

Are you ready for more?

Mai's first 2 steps could be combined into a single rotation.

1. Find the center and angle of this rotation.

2. Describe a general procedure for finding a center of rotation.

Lesson 13 Summary

The 3 rigid motions are reflect, translate, and rotate. Each of these rigid motions can be applied to any figure to create an image that is congruent. To do a rotation, we need to know 3 things: the center, the direction, and the angle.

Rotate $ABCD$ 90 degrees clockwise around point P.

Rotate EFG 120 degrees counterclockwise around point C.

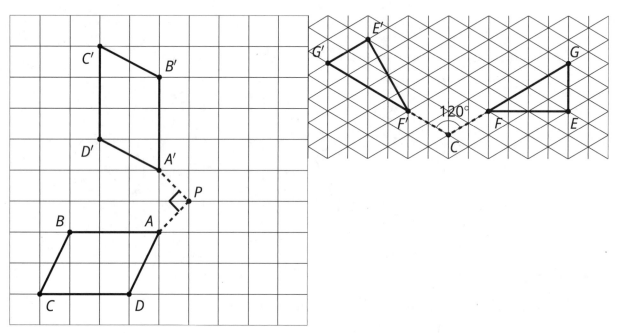

iM KH

Lesson 13 Practice Problems

1. Here are 2 polygons:

   Select **all** sequences of translations, rotations, and reflections below that would take polygon P to polygon Q.

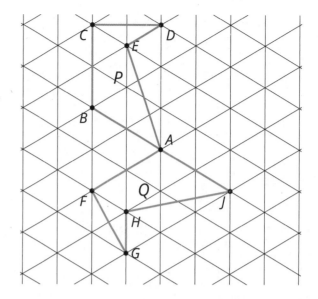

   A. Rotate 180° around point A.

   B. Rotate 60° counterclockwise around point A and then reflect over the line FA.

   C. Translate so that A is taken to J. Then reflect over line BA.

   D. Reflect over line BA and then translate by directed line segment BA.

   E. Reflect over the line BA and then rotate 60° counterclockwise around point A.

2. The semaphore alphabet is a way to use flags to signal messages. Here's how to signal the letter Q. Describe a transformation that would take the left hand flag to the right hand flag.

3. Match the directed line segment with the image of Polygon P being transformed to Polygon Q by translation by that directed line segment.

Translation 1

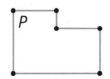 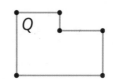

Translation 2

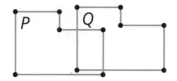

Translation 3

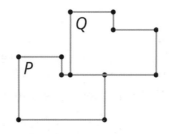

Translation 4

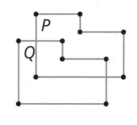

A. w

B. a

C. v

D. u

1. Translation 1

2. Translation 2

3. Translation 3

4. Translation 4

(From Unit 1, Lesson 12.)

iM KH

4. Draw the image of quadrilateral $ABCD$ when translated by the directed line segment v. Label the image of A as A', the image of B as B', the image of C as C', and the image of D as D'.

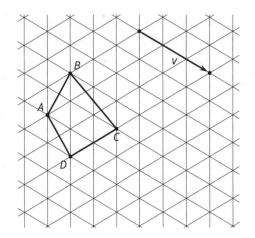

(From Unit 1, Lesson 12.)

5. Here is a line ℓ.

Plot 2 points, A and B, which stay in the same place when they are reflected over ℓ. Plot 2 other points, C and D, which move when they are reflected over ℓ.

(From Unit 1, Lesson 11.)

6. Here are 3 points in the plane. Select **all** the straightedge and compass constructions needed to locate the point that is the same distance from all 3 points.

   A. Construct the bisector of angle CAB.

   B. Construct the bisector of angle CBA.

   C. Construct the perpendicular bisector of BC.

   D. Construct the perpendicular bisector of AB.

   E. Construct a line perpendicular to AB through point C.

   F. Construct a line perpendicular to BC through point A.

(From Unit 1, Lesson 9.)

7. This straightedge and compass construction shows quadrilateral $ABCD$. Is $ABCD$ a rhombus? Explain how you know.

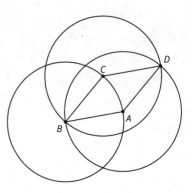

(From Unit 1, Lesson 7.)

Lesson 14: Defining Rotations

- Let's rotate shapes precisely.

14.1: Math Talk: Comparing Angles

For each figure, which pair of angles appears congruent? How could you check?

Figure 1

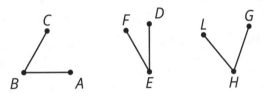

Figure 2

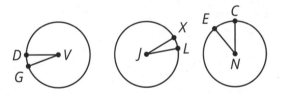

Figure 3

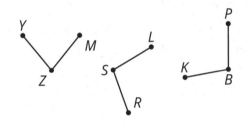

Figure 4

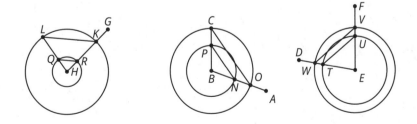

14.2: Info Gap: What's the Point: Rotations

Your teacher will give you either a problem card or a data card. Do not show or read your card to your partner.

If your teacher gives you the data card:

1. Silently read the information on your card.

2. Ask your partner "What specific information do you need?" and wait for your partner to ask for information. Only give information that is on your card. (Do not figure out anything for your partner!)

3. Before telling your partner the information, ask "Why do you need to know (that piece of information)?"

4. Read the problem card, and solve the problem independently.

5. Share the data card, and discuss your reasoning.

If your teacher gives you the problem card:

1. Silently read your card and think about what information you need to answer the question.

2. Ask your partner for the specific information that you need.

3. Explain to your partner how you are using the information to solve the problem.

4. When you have enough information, share the problem card with your partner, and solve the problem independently.

5. Read the data card, and discuss your reasoning.

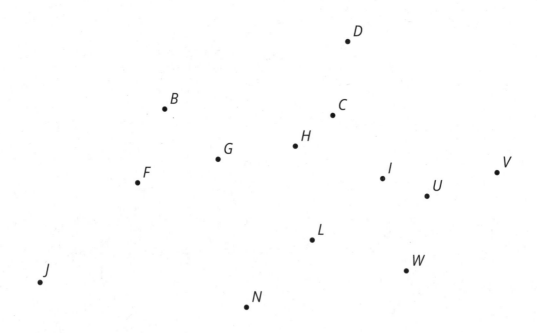

14.3: Turning into Triangles

1. Draw a segment. Label the endpoints A and B.

   a. Rotate segment AB clockwise around center B by 90 degrees. Label the new endpoint A'.

   b. Connect A to A' and lightly shade in the resulting triangle.

   c. What kind of triangle did you draw? What other properties do you notice in the figure? Explain your reasoning.

2. Draw a segment. Label the endpoints C and D.

   a. Rotate segment CD counterclockwise around center D by 30 degrees. Label the new endpoint C'.

   b. Rotate segment $C'D$ counterclockwise around center D by 30 degrees. Label the new endpoint C''.

   c. Connect C to C'' and lightly shade in the resulting triangle.

   d. What kind of triangle did you draw? What other properties do you notice in the figure? Explain your reasoning.

Are you ready for more?

You constructed an equilateral triangle by rotating a given segment around one of its endpoints by a specific angle measure. An equilateral triangle is an example of a *regular polygon*: a polygon with all sides congruent and all interior angles congruent. Try to construct some other regular polygons with this method.

Lesson 14 Summary

A **rotation** is a transformation with a center, an angle, and a direction (clockwise or counterclockwise).

Here is how a rotation with a center point C, an angle that measures t degrees, and a counterclockwise direction transforms a point P:

- The rotation sends point P to a point P' on the circle of radius CP.

- The angle PCP' measures t degrees and P' is counterclockwise around the circle from P.

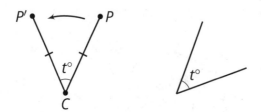

If the direction were clockwise instead, then P' would be clockwise around the circle of radius CP. If P and C are in the same place, then the rotation sends P to P' on the circle of radius zero, and so points P, C, and P' are all in the same place.

Glossary

- rotation

iM KH

Lesson 14 Practice Problems

1. Draw the image of quadrilateral $ABCD$ when rotated 120° counterclockwise around the point D.

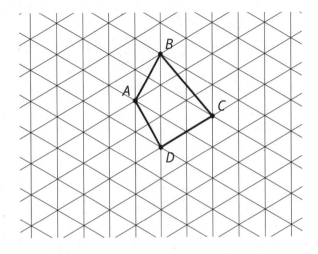

2. There is an equilateral triangle, ABC, inscribed in a circle with center D. What is the smallest angle you can rotate triangle ABC around D so that the image of A is B?

   A. 60°

   B. 90°

   C. 120°

   D. 180°

3. Which segment is the image of AB when rotated 90° counterclockwise around point P?

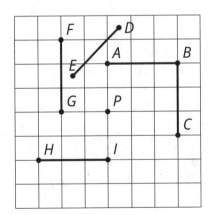

4. The semaphore alphabet is a way to use flags to signal **Q**
   messages. Here's how to signal the letter Q. Describe a
   transformation that would take the right hand flag to the
   left hand flag.

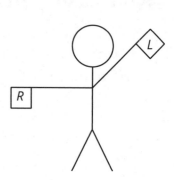

(From Unit 1, Lesson 13.)

5. Here are 2 polygons:

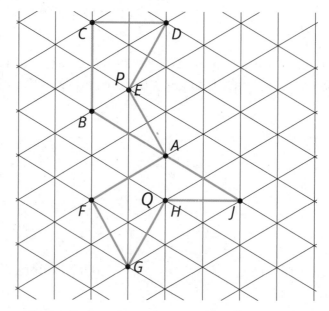

Select **all** sequences of translations, rotations, and reflections below that would take
polygon P to polygon Q.

A. Rotate 180° around point A.

B. Translate so that A is taken to J. Then reflect over line BA.

C. Rotate 60° counterclockwise around point A and then reflect over the line FA.

D. Reflect over the line BA and then rotate 60° counterclockwise around point A.

E. Reflect over line BA and then translate by directed line segment BA.

(From Unit 1, Lesson 13.)

iM **KH**

6. a. Draw the image of figure ABC when translated by directed line segment u. Label the image of A as A', the image of B as B', and the image of C as C'.

b. Explain why the line containing AB is parallel to the line containing $A'B'$.

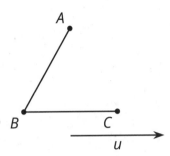

(From Unit 1, Lesson 12.)

7. There is a sequence of rigid transformations that takes A to A', B to B', and C to C'. The same sequence takes D to D'. Draw and label D':

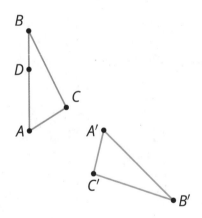

(From Unit 1, Lesson 10.)

Lesson 15: Symmetry

- Let's describe some symmetries of shapes.

15.1: Back to the Start

Here is a segment AB:

If you translate the segment up 5 units then down 5 units, it looks the same as it did originally.

1. What other rigid transformations create an image that fits exactly over the original segment?

2. Are there any *single* rigid motions that do the same thing?

iM KH

15.2: Self Reflection

Determine all the **lines of symmetry** for the shape your teacher assigns you. Create a visual display about your shape. Include these parts in your display:

- the name of your shape

- the definition of your shape

- drawings of each line of symmetry

- a description in words of each line of symmetry

- one non-example in a different color (a description and drawing of a reflection *not* over a line of symmetry)

Are you ready for more?

Look at all of the shapes the class explored and focus on those which had more than one line of symmetry.

1. What is true for all the lines of symmetry in these shapes?

2. Give an example of a shape that has two or more lines of symmetry that do not intersect at the same point.

3. What would happen if you did a sequence of two different reflections across lines of symmetry for the shapes you explored in class?

15.3: Diabolic Diagonals

Kiran thinks both diagonals of a kite are lines of symmetry. Tyler thinks only 1 diagonal is a line of symmetry. Who is correct? Explain how you know.

Lesson 15 Summary

A shape has **symmetry** if there is a rigid transformation which creates an image that fits exactly over the original shape. A shape has **reflection symmetry** if there is a reflection that takes the shape to itself, and the line of reflection in this case is called a **line of symmetry**. A regular hexagon has many lines of symmetry. Here are 2 of them. What other lines create a reflection where the image is the same as the original figure?

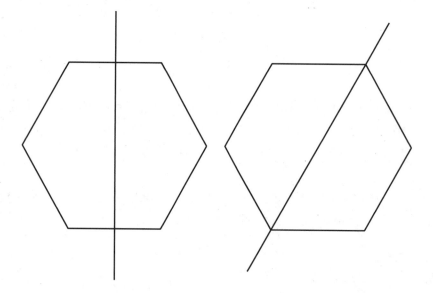

Glossary

- line of symmetry
- reflection symmetry
- symmetry

Lesson 15 Practice Problems

1. For each figure, identify any lines of symmetry the figure has.

2. In quadrilateral $BADC$, $AB = AD$ and $BC = DC$. The line AC is a line of symmetry for this quadrilateral.

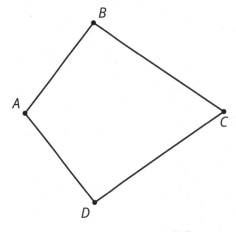

   a. Based on the line of symmetry, explain why the diagonals AC and BD are perpendicular.

   b. Based on the line of symmetry, explain why angles ABC and ADC have the same measure.

3. Three line segments form the letter Z. Rotate the letter Z counterclockwise around the midpoint of segment BC by 180 degrees. Describe the result.

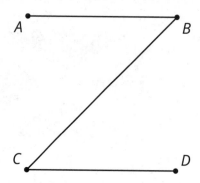

(From Unit 1, Lesson 14.)

4. There is a square, $ABCS$, inscribed in a circle with center D. What is the smallest angle we can rotate around D so that the image of A is B?

    A. 45°

    B. 60°

    C. 90°

    D. 180°

(From Unit 1, Lesson 14.)

5. Points A, B, C, and D are vertices of a square. Point E is inside the square. Explain how to tell whether point E is closer to A, B, C, or D.

(From Unit 1, Lesson 9.)

iM KH

6. Lines ℓ and m are perpendicular. $m \perp \ell$

Sometimes reflecting a point over m has
the same effect as rotating the point 180
degrees using center P. Select **all** labeled
points which have the same image for
both transformations.

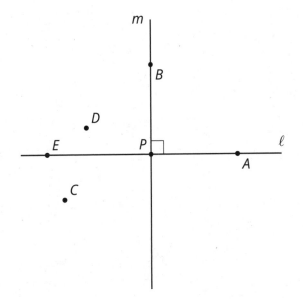

A. A

B. B

C. C

D. D

E. E

(From Unit 1, Lesson 11.)

7. Here is triangle *POG*. Match the description of the rotation with the image of *POG* under that rotation.

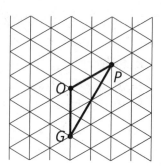

    A. Rotate 60 degrees clockwise around *O*.

    B. Rotate 120 degrees clockwise around *O*.

    C. Rotate 60 degrees counterclockwise around *O*.

    D. Rotate 60 degrees clockwise around *P*.

1.

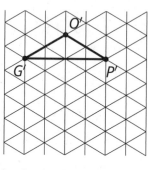

2.

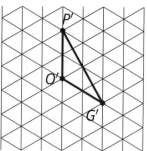

3.

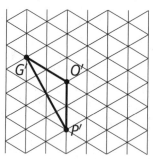

4.

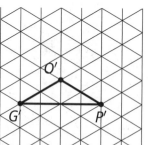

(From Unit 1, Lesson 13.)

iM KH

Lesson 16: More Symmetry

Let's describe more symmetries of shapes.

16.1: Which One Doesn't Belong: Symmetry

Which one doesn't belong?

A

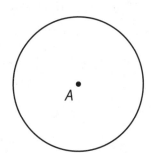

B

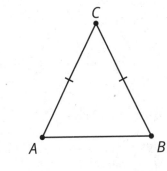

C

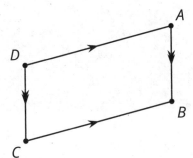

D

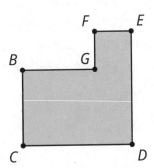

16.2: Self Rotation

Determine all the angles of rotation that create symmetry for the shape your teacher assigns you. Create a visual display about your shape. Include these parts in your display:

- the name of your shape

- the definition of your shape

- drawings of each rotation that creates symmetry

- a description in words of each rotation that creates symmetry, including the center, angle, and direction of rotation

- one non-example (a description and drawing of a rotation that does *not* result in symmetry)

Are you ready for more?

Finite figures, like the shapes we have looked at in class, cannot have translation symmetry. But with a pattern that continues on forever, it is possible. Patterns like this one that have translation symmetry in only one direction are called *frieze patterns*.

1. What are the lines of symmetry for this pattern?

2. What angles of rotation produce symmetry for this pattern?

3. What translations produce symmetry for this pattern if we imagine it extending horizontally forever?

16.3: Parallelogram Symmetry

Clare says, "Last class I thought the parallelogram would have reflection symmetry. I tried using a diagonal as the line of symmetry but it didn't work. So now I'm doubting that it has rotation symmetry."

iM KH

Lin says, "I thought that too at first, but now I think that a parallelogram *does* have rotation symmetry. Here, look at this."

How could Lin describe to Clare the symmetry she sees?

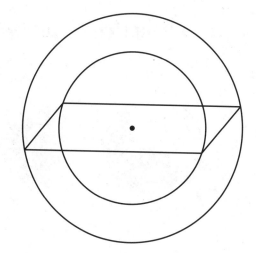

Lesson 16 Summary

A shape has **rotation symmetry** if there is a rotation between 0 and 360 degrees that takes the shape to itself. A regular hexagon has many angles that work to create rotation symmetry. Here is one of them. What other angles would create a rotation where the image is the same as the original figure?

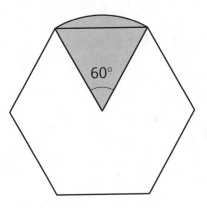

Can you think of a shape that has translation symmetry?

There aren't any polygons with translation symmetry, but an infinite shape like a line can be translated such that the translation takes the line to itself.

Glossary

- rotation symmetry

Lesson 16 Practice Problems

1. For each figure, identify any angles of rotation that create symmetry.

2. A triangle has rotation symmetry that can take any of its vertices to any of its other vertices. Select **all** conclusions that we can reach from this.

   A. All sides of the triangle have the same length.

   B. All angles of the triangle have the same measure.

   C. All rotations take one half of the triangle to the other half of the triangle.

3. Select **all** the angles of rotation that produce symmetry for this flower.

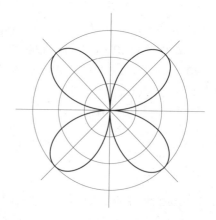

   A. 45 degrees

   B. 90 degrees

   C. 135 degrees

   D. 180 degrees

   E. 225 degrees

   F. 270 degrees

iM KH

4. Identify any lines of symmetry the figure has.

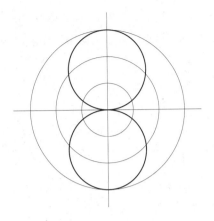

(From Unit 1, Lesson 15.)

5. A triangle has a line of symmetry. Select **all** conclusions that *must* be true.

   A. All sides of the triangle have the same length.

   B. All angles of the triangle have the same measure.

   C. No sides of the triangle have the same length.

   D. No angles of the triangle have the same measure.

   E. Two sides of the triangle have the same length.

   F. Two angles of the triangle have the same measure.

(From Unit 1, Lesson 15.)

6. Here are 4 triangles that have each been transformed by a different transformation. Which transformation is *not* a rigid transformation?

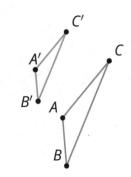

A.

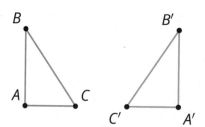

B.

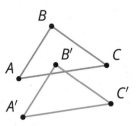

C.

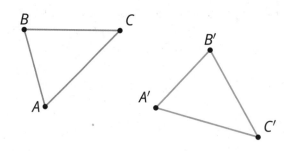

D.

(From Unit 1, Lesson 10.)

iM KH

7. Match each directed line segment with the translation from Polygon P to Polygon Q by that directed line segment.

Translation 1   **Translation 2**   **Translation 3**   **Translation 4**

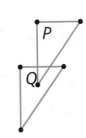 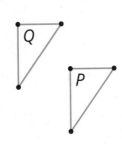

1. Translation 1

2. Translation 2

3. Translation 3

4. Translation 4

A.

v

B.

a

C.

u

D.

w

(From Unit 1, Lesson 12.)

Lesson 17: Working with Rigid Transformations

- Let's compare transformed figures.

17.1: Math Talk: From Here to There

Segment CD is the perpendicular bisector of segment AB. Find each transformation mentally.

A transformation that takes A to B.

A transformation that takes B to A.

A transformation that takes C to D.

A transformation that takes D to C.

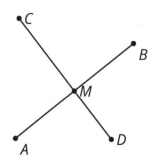

17.2: Card Sort: How Did This Get There?

1. Your teacher will give you a set of cards that show transformations of figures.

   a. Sort the cards into categories of your choosing. Be prepared to explain the meaning of your categories.

   b. Then sort the cards into categories in a different way. Be prepared to explain the meaning of your new categories.

2. For each card with a rigid transformation: write a sequence of rotations, translations, and reflections to get from the original figure to the image. Be precise.

Are you ready for more?

Diego observes that although it was often easier to use a sequence of reflections, rotations, and translations to describe the rigid transformations in the cards, each of them could be done with just a single reflection, rotation, or translation. However, Priya draws her own card, shown, which she claims can not be done as a single reflection, rotation, or translation.

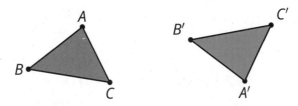

1. For each rigid transformation from the card sort, write the transformation as a single reflection, rotation, or translation.

2. Justify why Priya's transformation cannot be written as a single reflection, rotation, or translation.

17.3: Reflecting on Reflection

Diego says, "I see why a reflection could take $RSTU$ to $R'S'T'U'$, but I'm not sure where the line of reflection is. I'll just guess."

1. How could Diego see that a reflection could work without knowing where the line of reflection is?

2. How could Diego find an exact line of reflection that would work?

Lesson 17 Summary

If 2 figures are congruent, we can always find a rigid transformation that takes one onto the other.

Look at congruent figures ABC and DEF. It looks like DEF might be a reflection and translation of ABC. But is there a way to describe a sequence of transformations without guessing where the line of reflection might be?

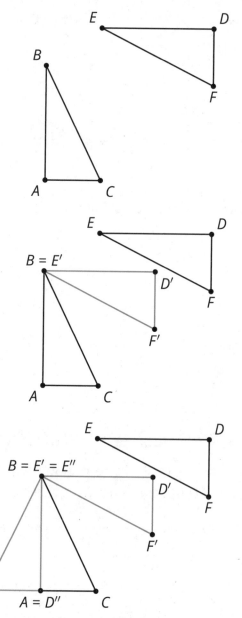

Our goal is to take the image of E onto B. Then we want to take the image of D onto A without moving E and B. Finally, we need to take the image of F onto C without moving any of the matching points.

We can start with translation: Translate triangle DEF by the directed line segment from E to B.

Now, a pair of corresponding points coincides. Is there a transformation we could use to take D' onto A that leaves B and E' in place? Rotations have a fixed point, so rotate triangle $D'E'F'$ by angle $D'BA$ using point B as the center.

Now, 2 pairs of corresponding points coincide. Reflecting across line AB will take $D''E''F''$ onto ABC, which is what we were trying to do. We know D'' and E'' won't move, since points on the line of reflection don't move. How do we know F'' will end up on C? Since the triangles are congruent, F'' and C are the same distance from the line of reflection.

iM KH

It is always possible to describe transformations using existing points, angles, and segments. It could take an extra step, but we can be confident transformations work if we don't guess where the line of reflection or center of rotation might be.

Lesson 17 Practice Problems

1. Quadrilateral $ABCD$ is congruent to quadrilateral $A'B'C'D'$. Describe a sequence of rigid motions that takes A to A', B to B', C to C', and D to D'.

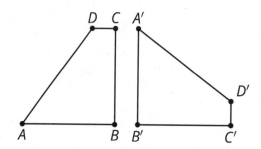

2. Select **all** transformations that must take any point A to any point B.

   A. Rotation of $180°$ around A

   B. Rotation of $180°$ around B

   C. Rotation of $180°$ around the midpoint of segment AB

   D. Reflection across the line AB

   E. Reflection across the perependicular bisector of segment AB

   F. Translation by the directed line segment AB

   G. Translation by the directed line segment BA

3. Triangle ABC is congruent to triangle $A'B'C'$. Describe a sequence of rigid motions that takes A to A', B to B', and C to C'.

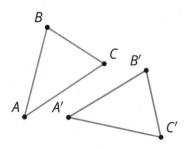

iM KH

4. A triangle has rotation symmetry that can take any of its vertices to any of its other vertices. Select **all** conclusions that we can reach from this.

   A. All sides of the triangle have the same length.

   B. All angles of the triangle have the same measure.

   C. All rotations take one half of the triangle to the other half of the triangle.

   D. It is a right triangle.

   E. None of the sides of the triangle have the same length.

   F. None of the angles of the triangle have the same measure.

   (From Unit 1, Lesson 16.)

5. Select **all** the angles of rotation that produce symmetry for this flower.

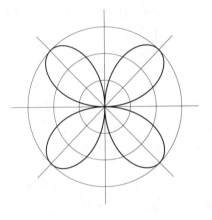

   A. 30

   B. 45

   C. 60

   D. 90

   E. 120

   F. 135

   G. 180

   (From Unit 1, Lesson 16.)

6. A right triangle has a line of symmetry. Select **all** conclusions that *must* be true.

   A. All sides of the triangle have the same length.

   B. All angles of the triangle have the same measure.

   C. Two sides of the triangle have the same length.

   D. Two angles of the triangle have the same measure.

   E. No sides of the triangle have the same length.

   F. No angles of the triangle have the same measure.

   (From Unit 1, Lesson 15.)

7. In quadrilateral $BADC$, $AB = AD$ and $BC = DC$. The line AC is a line of symmetry for this quadrilateral. Based on the line of symmetry, explain why angles ACB and ACD have the same measure.

   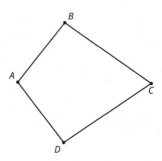

   (From Unit 1, Lesson 15.)

8. Which of these constructions would construct a line of reflection that takes the point A to point B?

   A. Construct the midpoint of segment AB.

   B. Construct the perpendicular bisector of segment AB.

   C. Construct a line tangent to circle A with radius AB.

   D. Construct a vertical line passing through point A and a horizontal line passing through point B.

   (From Unit 1, Lesson 11.)

iM KH

9. Here is triangle POG. Match the description of the rotation with the image of POG under that rotation.

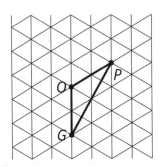

A. Rotate 300 degrees clockwise around O.

B. Rotate 60 degrees clockwise around O.

C. Rotate 60 degrees clockwise around P.

D. Rotate 240 degrees counterclockwise around O.

1.

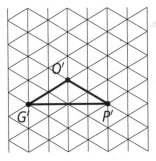

2.

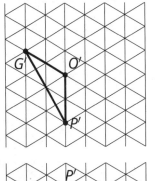

3.

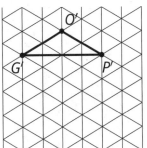

4.

(From Unit 1, Lesson 13.)

Lesson 18: Practicing Point by Point Transformations

Let's figure out some transformations.

18.1: Notice and Wonder: Obstacles

What do you notice? What do you wonder?

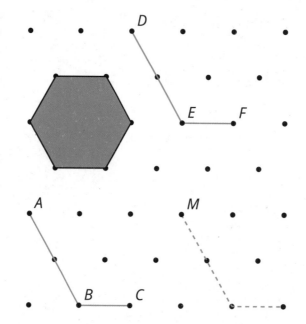

iM KH

18.2: Obstacle Course

For each diagram, find a sequence of translations and rotations that take the original figure to the image, so that if done physically, the figure would not touch any of the solid obstacles and would not leave the diagram. Test your sequence by drawing the image of each step.

1. Take ABC to DEF.

2. Take GHI to JKL.

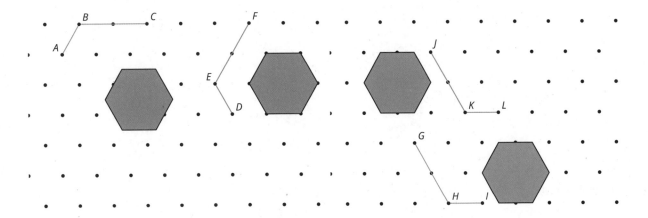

Are you ready for more?

Create your own obstacle course with an original figure, an image, and at least one obstacle. Make sure it is possible to solve. Challenge a partner to solve your obstacle course.

18.3: Point by Point

For each question, describe a sequence of translations, rotations, and reflections that will take parallelogram $ABCD$ to parallelogram $A'B'C'D'$.

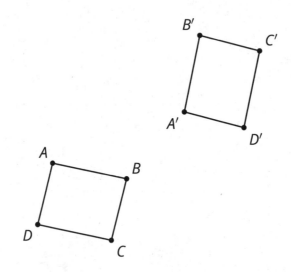

1.

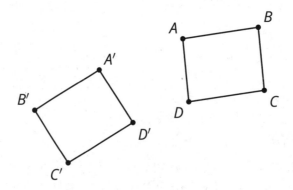

2.

Are you ready for more?

In this unit, we have been focusing on rigid transformations in two dimensions. By thinking carefully about precise definitions, we can extend many of these ideas into three dimensions. How could you define rotations, reflections, and translations in three dimensions?

iM KH

Lesson 18 Summary

Sometimes it's not hard to figure out a transformation that takes all the points of one figure directly to all the points of its image. Here, it looks like there is a 90 degree rotation that will take figure $ABCD$ to figure $EFGH$. It is not obvious where the center of rotation would be, though.

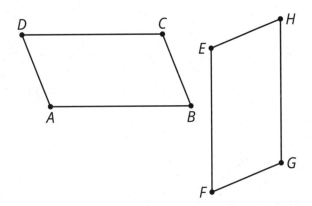

Instead, we could describe the transformation in 2 steps. First, translate figure $ABCD$ by the directed line segment AE. Next, rotate the image of $ABCD$ clockwise by angle $B'EF$ using center E. It looks like this is a 90 degree rotation, but we can be sure the rotation will work if we use the labels to define the rotation instead of an angle measure. This method of matching up 1 point at a time until the whole figure has been taken to the image will work for any transformation, including ones in which it's hard to see a single transformation from one figure to the other.

Lesson 18 Practice Problems

1. The figures are congruent. Select **all** the sequences of transformations that would take Figure 1 to Figure 2.

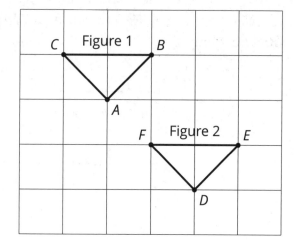

A. Translate by directed line segment AD.

B. Rotate 180 degrees around point E.

C. Translate by directed line segment AE and reflect across AC.

D. Translate by directed line segment CE and rotate 90 degrees counterclockwise around point E.

E. Rotate 180 degrees around point C, translate by directed line segment CE, and reflect across segment EF.

F. Reflect across segment AB, rotate clockwise by angle BFE using center F, then reflect across segment EF.

2. a. Draw the image of figure $ACTS$ after a clockwise rotation around point T using angle CTS and then a translation by directed line segment CT.

   b. Describe another sequence of transformations that will result in the same image.

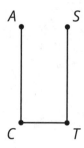

iM KH

3. Draw the image of triangle ABC after this sequence of rigid transformations.

   a. Reflect across line segment AB.

   b. Translate by directed line segment u.

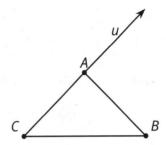

4. Describe a transformation that takes any point A to any point B.

(From Unit 1, Lesson 17.)

5. Triangle ABC is congruent to triangle $A'B'C'$. Describe a sequence of rigid motions that takes A to A', B to B', and C to C'.

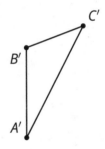

(From Unit 1, Lesson 17.)

6. A quadrilateral has rotation symmetry that can take any of its vertices to any of its other vertices. Select **all** conclusions that we can reach from this.

   A. All sides of the quadrilateral have the same length.

   B. All angles of the quadrilateral have the same measure.

   C. All rotations take one half of the quadrilateral to the other half of the quadrilateral.

(From Unit 1, Lesson 16.)

7. A quadrilateral has a line of symmetry. Select **all** conclusions that *must* be true.

   A. All sides of the quadrilateral have the same length.

   B. All angles of the quadrilateral have the same measure.

   C. Two sides of the quadrilateral have the same length.

   D. Two angles of the quadrilateral have the same measure.

   E. No sides of the quadrilateral have the same length.

   F. No angles of the quadrilateral have the same measure.

   (From Unit 1, Lesson 15.)

8. Which segment is the image of FG when rotated 90° clockwise around point P?

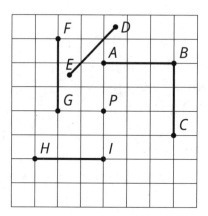

   (From Unit 1, Lesson 14.)

9. Which statement is true about a translation?

   A. A translation rotates a line.

   B. A translation takes a line to a parallel line or itself.

   C. A translation takes a line to a perpendicular line.

   D. A translation dilates a line.

   (From Unit 1, Lesson 12.)

iM KH

Lesson 19: Evidence, Angles, and Proof

- Let's make convincing explanations.

19.1: Math Talk: Supplementary Angles

Mentally evaluate all of the missing angle measures in each figure.

Figure A

Figure B

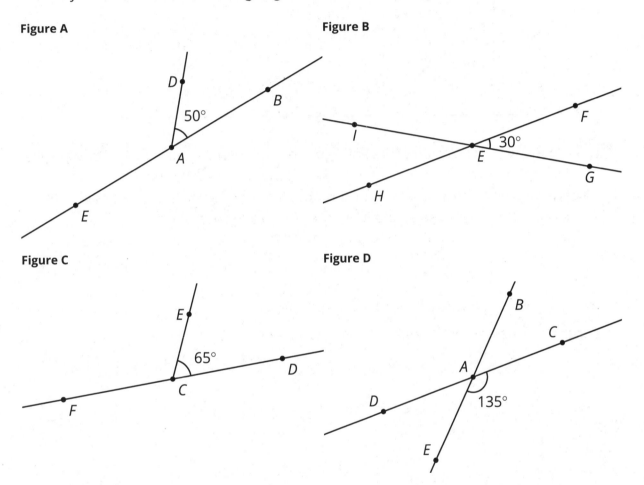

Figure C

Figure D

19.2: That Can't Be Right, Can It?

Here is a figure where ray r meets line ℓ. The dashed rays are angle bisectors.

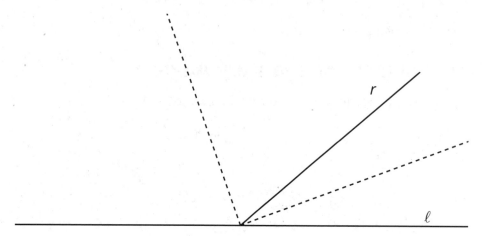

1. Diego made the conjecture: "The angle formed between the angle bisectors is always a right angle, no matter what the angle between r and ℓ is." It is difficult to tell specifically which angles Diego is talking about in his conjecture. Label the diagram and rephrase Diego's conjecture more precisely using your labels.

2. Is the conjecture true? Explain your reasoning.

19.3: Convince Me

Here are 2 intersecting lines that create 2 pairs of vertical angles:

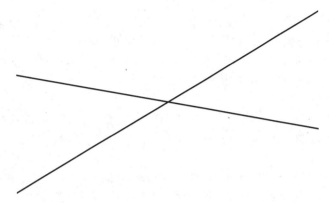

1. What is the relationship between vertical angles? Write down a conjecture. Label the diagram to make it easier to write your conjecture precisely.

2. How do you know your conjecture is true for all possible pairs of vertical angles? Explain your reasoning.

Are you ready for more?

One reason mathematicians like to have rigorous proofs even when conjectures seem to be true is that sometimes conjectures that are made turn out to not be true. Here is one famous example. If we draw n points on a circle and connect each pair of points how many regions does that divide the circle into? If we draw only 1 point there are no line segments to connect and so just 1 region in the circle. If we draw 2 points they are connected by a line segment which divides the circle into 2 regions.

1. If we draw 3 points on a circle and connect each pair of points with a line segment how many regions do we get in our circle?

2. If we draw 4 points on a circle and connect each pair of points with a line segment how many regions do we get in our circle?

3. If we draw 5 points on a circle and connect each pair of points with a line segment how many regions do we get in our circle?

4. Make a conjecture about how many regions we get if we draw n points on a circle and connect each pair of points with a line segment.

5. Test your conjecture with 6 points on a circle. How many regions do we get?

Lesson 19 Summary

In many situations, it is important to understand the reasons why an idea is true. Here are some questions to ask when trying to convince ourselves or others that a statement is true:

- How do we know this is true?

- Would these reasons convince someone who didn't think it was true?

- Is this true always, or only in certain cases?

- Can we find any situations where this is false?

In this lesson, we reasoned that pairs of vertical angles are always congruent to each other:

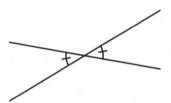

We saw this by labeling the diagram and making precise arguments having to do with transformations or angle relationships. For example, label the diagram with points:

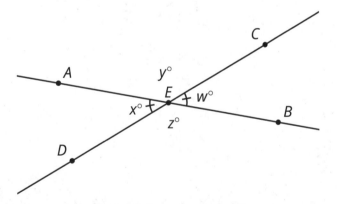

Rotate the figure 180 degrees around point E. Then ray EA goes to ray EB and ray ED goes to ray EC. That means the rotation takes angle AED onto angle BEC, and so angle AED is congruent to angle BEC.

Many true statements have multiple explanations. Another line of reasoning uses angle relationships. Notice that angles AED and AEC together form line CD. That means that $x + y = 180$. Similarly, $y + w = 180$. That means that both x and w are equal to $180 - y$, so they are equal to each other. Since angle AED and angle CEB have the same degree measure, they must be congruent.

Lesson 19 Practice Problems

1. What is the measure of angle ABE?

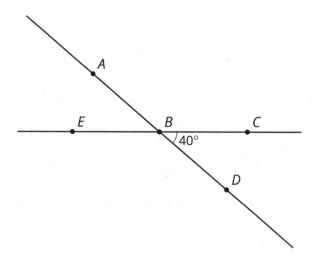

2. Select **all** true statements about the figure.

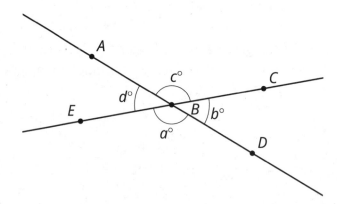

A. $c + b = d + c$

B. $d + b = 180$

C. Rotate clockwise by angle ABC using center B. Then angle CBD is the image of angle ABE.

D. Rotate 180 degrees using center B. Then angle CBD is the image of angle EBA.

E. Reflect across the angle bisector of angle ABC. Then angle CBD is the image of angle ABE.

F. Reflect across line CE. Then angle CBD is the image of angle EBA

iM KH

3. Point D is rotated 180 degrees using B as the center. Explain why the image of D must lie on the ray BA.

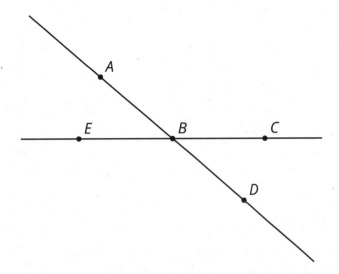

4. Draw the result of this sequence of transformations.

   a. Rotate $ABCD$ clockwise by angle ADC using point D as the center.

   b. Translate the image by the directed line segment DE.

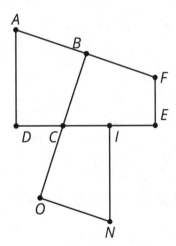

(From Unit 1, Lesson 18.)

5. Quadrilateral $ABCD$ is congruent to quadrilateral $A'B'C'D'$. Describe a sequence of rigid motions that takes A to A', B to B', C to C', and D to D'.

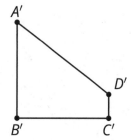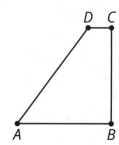

(From Unit 1, Lesson 17.)

6. Triangle ABC is congruent to triangle $A'B'C'$. Describe a sequence of rigid motions that takes A to A', B to B', and C to C'.

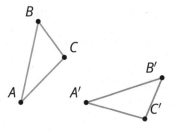

(From Unit 1, Lesson 17.)

7. In quadrilateral $BADC$, $AB = AD$ and $BC = DC$. The line AC is a line of symmetry for this quadrilateral.

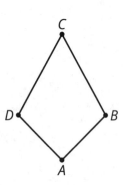

a. Based on the line of symmetry, explain why the diagonals AC and BD are perpendicular.

b. Based on the line of symmetry, explain why angles ACB and ACD have the same measure.

(From Unit 1, Lesson 15.)

iM KH

8. Here are 2 polygons:

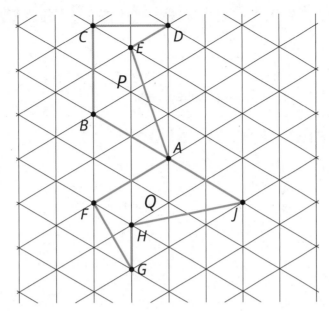

Select **all** sequences of translations, rotations, and reflections below that would take polygon P to polygon Q.

A. Reflect over line BA and then translate by directed line segment CB.

B. Translate by directed line segment BA then reflect over line BA.

C. Rotate 60° clockwise around point B and then translate by directed line segment CB.

D. Translate so that E is taken to H. Then rotate 120° clockwise around point H.

E. Translate so that A is taken to J. Then reflect over line BA.

(From Unit 1, Lesson 13.)

Lesson 20: Transformations, Transversals, and Proof

- Let's prove statements about parallel lines.

20.1: Math Talk: Angle Relationships

Lines ℓ and m are parallel. Mentally evaluate the measure x in each figure.

Figure A

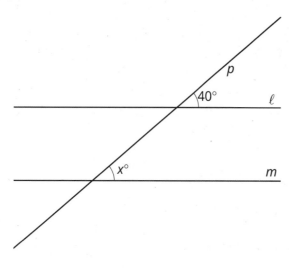

Figure B

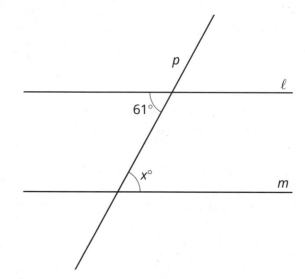

Figure C

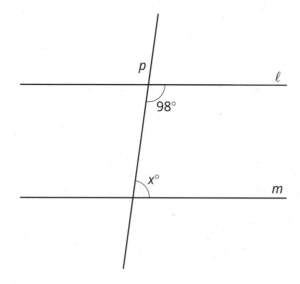

Figure D

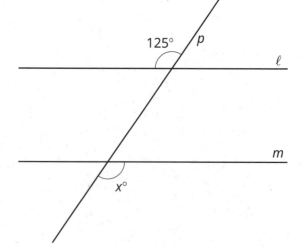

iM KH

20.2: Make a Mark? Give a Reason.

Here are intersecting lines AE and CD:

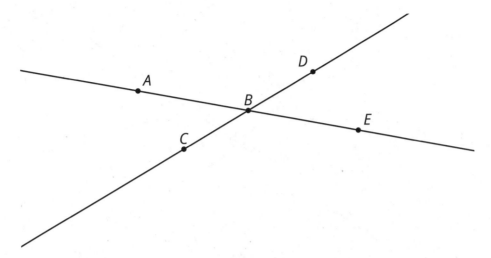

1. Translate lines AE and CD by the directed line segment from B to C. Label the images of A, B, C, D, E as A', B', C', D', E'.

2. What is true about lines AE and $A'E'$? Explain your reasoning.

3. Take turns with your partner to identify congruent angles.
   a. For each pair of congruent angles that you find, explain to your partner how you know the angles are congruent.

   b. For each match that your partner finds, listen carefully to their explanation. If you disagree, discuss your thinking and work to reach an agreement.

20.3: An Alternate Explanation

Here are intersecting lines AE and CD:

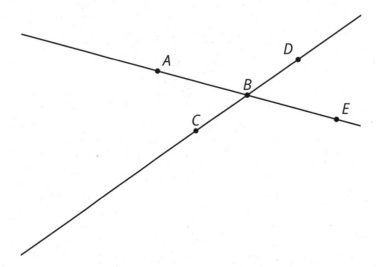

1. Rotate line AE by 180 degrees around point C. Label the images of A, B, C, D, E as A', B', C', D', E'.

2. What is true about lines AB and $A'B'$? Explain your reasoning.

3. Take turns with your partner to identify congruent angles.

   a. For each pair of congruent angles that you find, explain to your partner how you know the angles are congruent.

   b. For each match that your partner finds, listen carefully to their explanation. If you disagree, discuss your thinking and work to reach an agreement.

iM KH

Are you ready for more?

1. Prove that 180 degree rotations take lines that do not pass through the center of rotation to parallel lines.

2. What is the image of a line that is rotated 180 degrees around a point on the line?

Lesson 20 Summary

There are often several different ways to explain why statements are true. Comparing the different ways can lead to new insights or more flexible understanding. Consider the angles formed when 2 parallel lines ℓ and m are cut by a transversal:

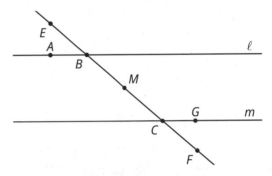

Suppose we want to explain why angle ABE is congruent to angle GCF. Label the midpoint of BC as M. Rotating 180 degrees around M takes angle ABE to angle GCF. Why? Well, B and C are equidistant from M, so the rotation takes B to C. Also, it takes the transversal to itself, so it takes the ray BE to the ray CF. Finally, the rotation takes line ℓ onto line m because 180 degree rotations take lines onto parallel lines and m is the only line parallel to ℓ that also goes through C.

A different explanation can prove the same fact using a translation and the idea that vertical angles are congruent. Try thinking of that explanation yourself.

Lesson 20 Practice Problems

1. Priya: I bet if the alternate interior angles are congruent, then the lines will have to be parallel.

   Han: Really? We know if the lines are parallel then the alternate interior angles are congruent, but I didn't know that it works both ways.

   Priya: Well, I think so. What if angle ABC and angle BCJ are both 40 degrees? If I draw a line perpendicular to line AI through point B, I get this triangle. Angle CBX would be 50 degrees because $40 + 50 = 90$. And because the angles of a triangle sum to 180 degrees, angle CXB is 90 degrees. It's also a right angle!

   Han: Oh! Then line AI and line GJ are both perpendicular to the same line. That's how we constructed parallel lines, by making them both perpendicular to the same line. So lines AI and GJ must be parallel.

   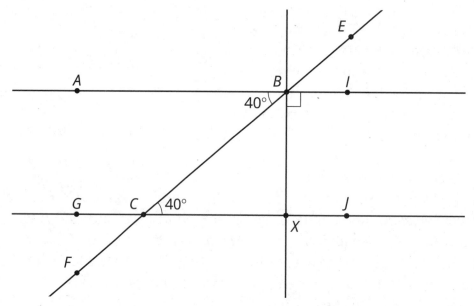

   a. Label the diagram based on Priya and Han's conversation.

   b. Is there something special about 40 degrees? Will any 2 lines cut by a transversal with congruent alternate interior angles, be parallel?

iM KH

2. Prove lines AI and GJ are parallel.

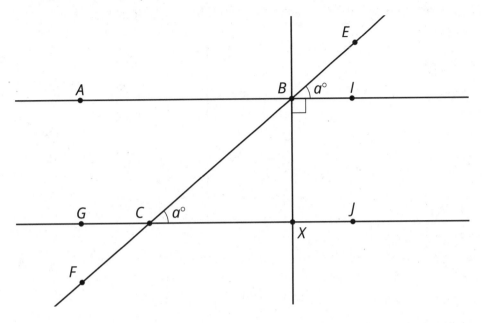

3. What is the measure of angle ABE?

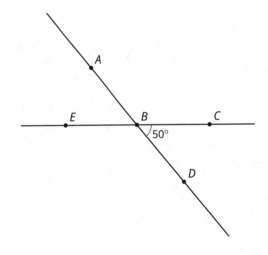

(From Unit 1, Lesson 19.)

4. Lines AB and BC are perpendicular. The dashed rays bisect angles ABD and CBD. Explain why the measure of angle EBF is 45 degrees.

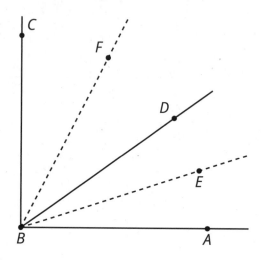

(From Unit 1, Lesson 19.)

5. Identify a figure that is *not* the image of quadrilateral $ABCD$ after a sequence of transformations. Explain how you know.

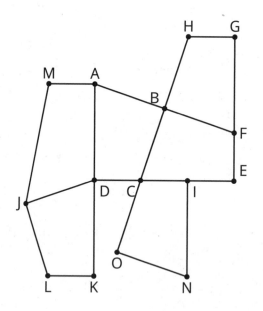

(From Unit 1, Lesson 18.)

iM KH

6. Quadrilateral $ABCD$ is congruent to quadrilateral $A'B'C'D'$. Describe a sequence of rigid motions that takes A to A', B to B', C to C', and D to D'.

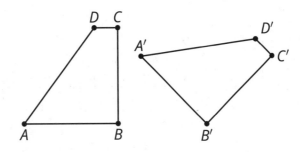

(From Unit 1, Lesson 17.)

7. Triangle ABC is congruent to triangle $A'B'C'$. Describe a sequence of rigid motions that takes A to A', B to B', and C to C'.

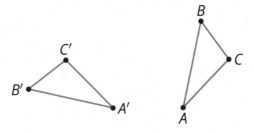

(From Unit 1, Lesson 17.)

8. Identify any angles of rotation that create symmetry.

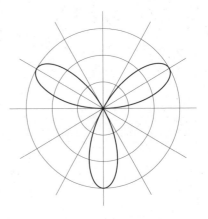

(From Unit 1, Lesson 16.)

9. Select **all** the angles of rotation that produce symmetry for this flower.

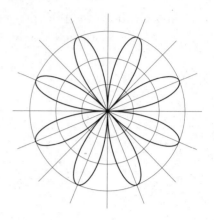

A. 45

B. 60

C. 90

D. 120

E. 135

F. 150

G. 180

(From Unit 1, Lesson 16.)

10. Three line segments form the letter N. Rotate the letter N clockwise around the midpoint of segment BC by 180 degrees. Describe the result.

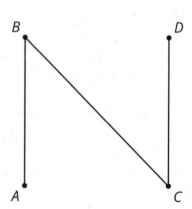

(From Unit 1, Lesson 14.)

iM KH

Lesson 21: One Hundred and Eighty

- Let's prove the Triangle Angle Sum Theorem.

21.1: What Went Wrong?

Here are 2 lines ℓ and m that are *not* parallel that have been cut by a transversal.

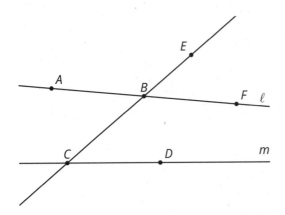

Tyler thinks angle EBF is congruent to angle BCD because they are corresponding angles and a translation along the directed line segment from B to C would take one angle onto the other. Here are his reasons.

- The translation takes B onto C, so the image of B is C.

- The translation takes E somewhere on ray CB because it would need to be translated by a distance greater than BC to land on the other side of C.

- The image of F has to land somewhere on line m because translations take lines to parallel lines and line m is the only line parallel to ℓ that goes through B'.

- The image of F, call it F', has to land on the right side of line BC or else line FF' wouldn't be parallel to the directed line segment from B to C.

1. Your teacher will assign you one of Tyler's statements to think about. Is the statement true? Explain your reasoning.

2. In what circumstances are corresponding angles congruent? Be prepared to share your reasoning.

21.2: Triangle Angle Sum One Way

1. Use a straightedge to create a triangle. Label the 3 angle measures as $a°$, $b°$, and $c°$.

2. Use paper folding to mark the midpoints of 2 of the sides.

3. Extend the side of the triangle without the midpoint in both directions to make a line.

4. Use what you know about rotations to create a line parallel to the line you made that goes through the opposite vertex.

5. What is the value of $a + b + c$? Explain your reasoning.

iM KH

21.3: Triangle Angle Sum Another Way

Here is triangle ABC with angle measures $a°$, $b°$, and $c°$. Each side has been extended to a line.

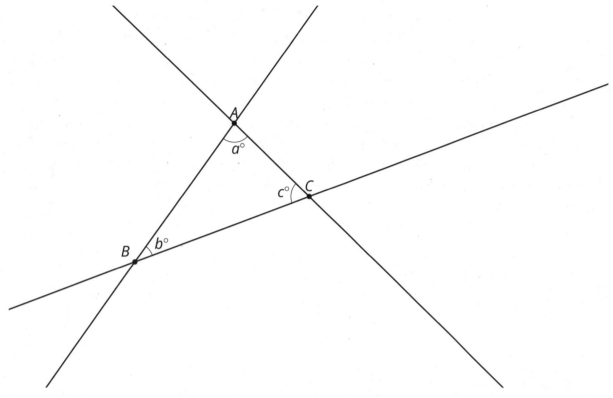

1. Translate triangle ABC along the directed line segment from B to C to make triangle $A'B'C'$. Label the measures of the angles in triangle $A'B'C'$.

2. Translate triangle $A'B'C'$ along the directed line segment from A' to C to make triangle $A''B''C''$. Label the measures of the angles in triangle $A''B''C''$.

3. Label the measures of the angles that meet at point C. Explain your reasoning.

4. What is the value of $a + b + c$? Explain your reasoning.

Are you ready for more?

One reason mathematicians like to have rigorous proofs even when conjectures seem to be true is that it can help reveal what assertions were used. This can open up new areas to explore if we change those assumptions. For example, both of our proofs that the measures of the angles of a triangle sum to 180 degree were based on rigid transformations that take lines to parallel lines. If our assumptions about parallel lines changed, so would the consequences about triangle angle sums. Any study of geometry where these assumptions change is called non-Euclidean geometry. In some non-Euclidean geometries, lines in the same direction may intersect while in others they do not. In spherical geometry, which studies curved surfaces like the surface of Earth, lines in the same direction always intersect. This has amazing consequences for triangles. Imagine a triangle connecting the north pole, a point on the equator, and a second point on the equator one quarter of the way around Earth from the first. What is the sum of the angles in this triangle?

Lesson 21 Summary

Using rotations and parallel lines, we can understand why the angles in a triangle always add to 180 degrees. Here is triangle ABC.

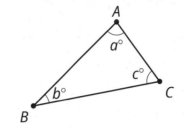

Rotate triangle ABC 180 degrees around the midpoint of segment AB and label the image of C as D. Then rotate triangle ABC 180 degrees around the midpoint of segment AC and label the image of B as E.

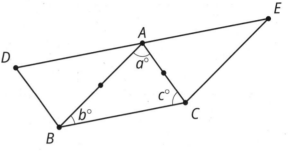

Note that each 180 degree rotation takes line BC to a parallel line. So line DA is parallel to BC and line AE is also parallel to BC. There is only one line parallel to BC that goes through point A, so lines DA and AE are the same line. Since line DE is parallel to line BC, we know that alternate interior angles are congruent. That means that angle BAD also measures $b°$ and angle CAE also measures $c°$.

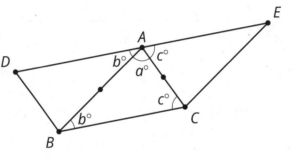

Since DE is a line, the 3 angle measures at point A must sum to 180 degrees. So $a + b + c = 180$. This argument does not depend on the triangle we started with, so that proves the sum of the 3 angle measures of *any* triangle is always 180 degrees.

Lesson 21 Practice Problems

1. The triangles here are each obtained by applying rigid motions to triangle 1.

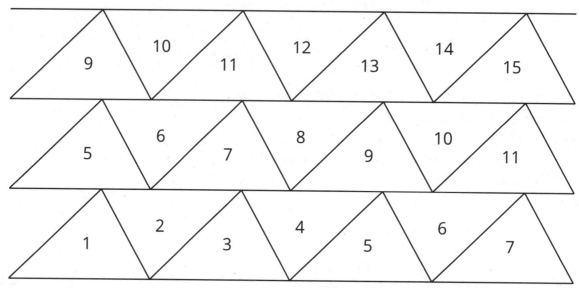

   a. Which triangles are translations of triangle 1? Explain how you know.

   b. Which triangles are not translations of triangle 1? Explain how you know.

2. The quadrilateral is a parallelogram.
   Find the measure of angles 1, 2, and 3.

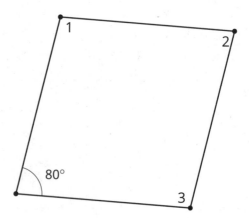

iM KH

3. In the figure shown, lines f and g are parallel. Select the angle that is congruent to angle 1.

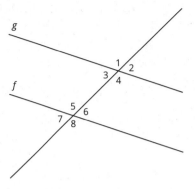

A. Angle 2

B. Angle 6

C. Angle 7

D. Angle 8

(From Unit 1, Lesson 20.)

4. Angle BDE is congruent to angle BAC. Name another pair of congruent angles. Explain how you know.

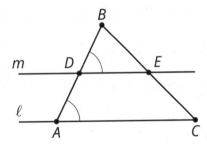

(From Unit 1, Lesson 20.)

5. a. Describe a transformation that could be used to show that corresponding angles are congruent.

   b. Describe a transformation that could be used to show that alternate interior angles are congruent.

(From Unit 1, Lesson 20.)

6. Lines AD and EC meet at point B.

Which of these *must* be true? Select **all** that apply.

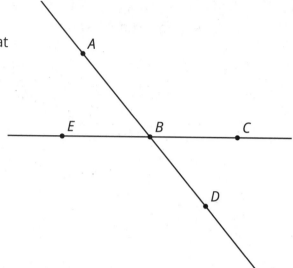

A. A 180 degree clockwise rotation using center B takes D to A.

B. The image of D after a 180 degree rotation using center B lies on ray BA.

C. If a 180 degree rotation using center B takes C to E then it also takes E to C.

D. Angle ABC is congruent to angle DBE.

E. Angle ABE is congruent to angle ABC.

(From Unit 1, Lesson 19.)

7. Points E, B, and C are collinear. Explain why points A, B, and D are collinear.

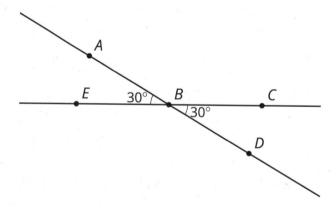

(From Unit 1, Lesson 19.)

iM KH

8.   a. Draw the image of figure $ACTS$ after a clockwise rotation around point C using angle CTS and then a translation by the directed line segment CT.

   b. Describe another sequence of transformations that will result in the same image.

(From Unit 1, Lesson 18.)

9. Triangle ABC is congruent to triangle $A'B'C'$. Describe a sequence of rigid motions that takes A to A', B to B', and C to C'.

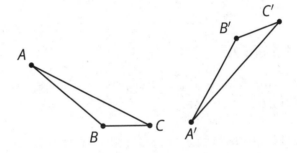

(From Unit 1, Lesson 17.)

Lesson 22: Now What Can You Build?

- Let's construct some creative shapes.

22.1: Notice and Wonder: Dramatic Designs

What do you notice? What do you wonder?

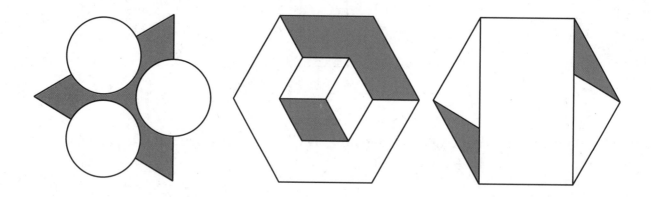

22.2: Duplicate a Design

Your teacher will give you a collection of designs that all began from the construction of a regular hexagon. Choose one to use.

1. Record any rigid motions (rotation, reflection, or translation) you see in your design.

2. Use straightedge and compass moves to recreate the design.

3. Write down instructions for how to construct it.

iM KH

22.3: Make Your Own Design

Use straightedge and compass moves to create a new design.

Write down the moves you followed on that same sheet of paper so someone else can recreate your design.

Are you ready for more?

Construct a tessellation with rotation, reflection, and translation symmetry.

22.4: Make Their Design

1. Follow the instructions to make a design.

2. List everything in the design that is congruent. Explain how you know.

Lesson 22 Summary

There is a deep connection between geometry and art. Using simple construction tools, it's possible to create beautiful patterns. Precisely recording instructions for a pattern allows other people to make the same pattern and enjoy it for themselves! These same ideas can be applied in three-dimensional space to create the objects we use and appreciate every day.

Lesson 22 Practice Problems

1. This design began from the construction of a regular hexagon. Name 2 pairs of congruent figures.

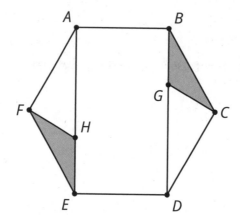

2. This design began from the construction of a regular hexagon. Describe a rigid motion that will take the figure to itself.

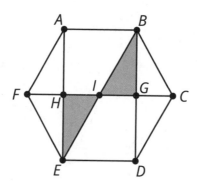

3. Noah starts with triangle ABC and makes 2 new triangles by translating B to A and by translating B to C. Noah thinks that triangle DCA is congruent to triangle BAC. Do you agree with Noah? Explain your reasoning.

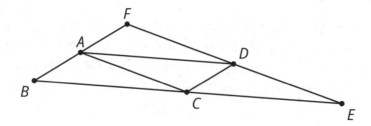

(From Unit 1, Lesson 21.)

iM KH

4. In the image, triangle ABC is congruent to triangle BAD and triangle CEA. What are the measures of the 3 angles in triangle CEA? Show or explain your reasoning.

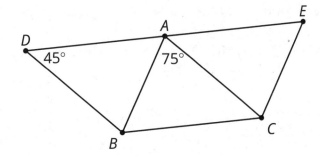

(From Unit 1, Lesson 21.)

5. In the figure shown, angle 3 is congrent to angle 6. Select **all** statements that *must* be true.

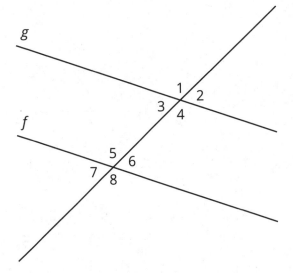

A. Lines f and g are parallel.

B. Angle 2 is congruent to angle 6

C. Angle 2 and angle 5 are supplementary

D. Angle 1 is congruent to angle 7

E. Angle 4 is congruent to angle 6

(From Unit 1, Lesson 20.)

6. In this diagram, point M is the midpoint of segment AC and B' is the image of B by a rotation of $180°$ around M.

a. Explain why rotating $180°$ using center M takes A to C.

b. Explain why angles BAC and $B'CA$ have the same measure.

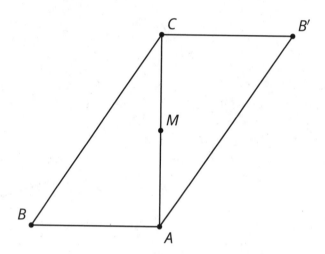

(From Unit 1, Lesson 20.)

7. Lines AB and BC are perpendicular. The dashed rays bisect angles ABD and CBD.

Select **all** statements that *must* be true:

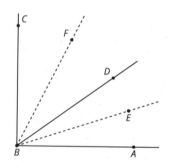

A. Angle CBF is congruent to angle DBF

B. Angle CBE is obtuse

C. Angle ABC is congruent to angle EBF

D. Angle DBC is congruent to angle EBF

E. Angle EBF is 45 degrees

(From Unit 1, Lesson 19.)

iM KH

8. Lines AD and EC meet at point B.

Give an example of a rotation using an angle greater than 0 degrees and less than 360 degrees, that takes both lines to themselves. Explain why your rotation works.

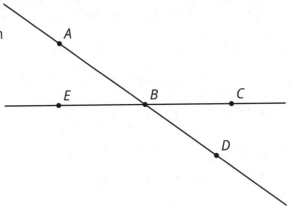

(From Unit 1, Lesson 19.)

9. Draw the image of triangle ABC after this sequence of rigid transformations.

    a. Reflect across line segment AB.

    b. Translate by directed line segment u.

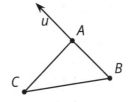

(From Unit 1, Lesson 18.)

10.   a. Draw the image of figure $CAST$ after a clockwise rotation around point T using angle CAS and then a translation by directed line segment AS.

    b. Describe another sequence of transformations that will result in the same image.

(From Unit 1, Lesson 18.)

Learning Targets

Lesson 1: Build It

- I can create diagrams using a straightedge.

- I know to use a compass to construct a circle.

Lesson 2: Constructing Patterns

- I can follow instructions to create a construction.

- I can use precise mathematical language to describe a construction.

Lesson 3: Construction Techniques 1: Perpendicular Bisectors

- I can construct a perpendicular bisector.

- I understand what is special about the set of points equidistant from two given points.

Lesson 4: Construction Techniques 2: Equilateral Triangles

- I can construct an equilateral triangle.

- I can identify congruent segments in figures and explain why they are congruent.

Lesson 5: Construction Techniques 3: Perpendicular Lines and Angle Bisectors

- I can construct a line that is perpendicular to a given line through a point on the line.

- I can construct an angle bisector.

Lesson 6: Construction Techniques 4: Parallel and Perpendicular Lines

- I can construct a parallel line through a given point.

- I can construct a perpendicular line through a given point.

Lesson 7: Construction Techniques 5: Squares

- I can construct a square inscribed in a circle.

- I can construct a square using a given segment for one of its sides.

Lesson 8: Using Technology for Constructions

- I can use technology to help me construct specific diagrams.

Lesson 9: Speedy Delivery

- I can construct perpendicular bisectors to help solve problems.

- I can use my geometry knowledge to solve problems.

Lesson 10: Rigid Transformations

- Given a figure and the description of a transformation, I can draw the figure's image after the transformation.

- I can describe the sequence of transformations necessary to take a figure onto another figure.

- I know that rigid transformations result in congruent figures.

Lesson 11: Defining Reflections

- I can describe a reflection by specifying the line of reflection.

- I can draw reflections.

Lesson 12: Defining Translations

- I can describe a translation by stating the directed line segment.

- I can draw translations.

Lesson 13: Incorporating Rotations

- Given a figure and the description of a transformation, I can draw the figure's image after the transformation.

- I can describe the sequence of transformations necessary to take a figure onto another figure.

- I know that rigid transformations result in congruent figures.

Lesson 14: Defining Rotations

- I can describe a rotation by stating the center and angle of rotation.

- I can draw rotations.

Lesson 15: Symmetry

- I can describe the reflections that take a figure onto itself.

Lesson 16: More Symmetry

- I can describe the rotations that take a figure onto itself.

Lesson 17: Working with Rigid Transformations

- I can describe a transformation that takes given points to another set of points.

Lesson 18: Practicing Point by Point Transformations

- Given a figure and the description of a transformation, I can draw the figure's image after the transformation.

- I can describe a transformation that takes given points to another set of points.

Lesson 19: Evidence, Angles, and Proof

- I can label and make conjectures from diagrams.

- I can prove vertical angles are congruent.

Lesson 20: Transformations, Transversals, and Proof

- I can prove alternate interior angles are congruent.

- I can prove corresponding angles are congruent.

Lesson 21: One Hundred and Eighty

- I can prove the angles in a triangle sum to 180 degrees.

Lesson 22: Now What Can You Build?

- I can follow directions to construct a pattern.

iM KH

GEOMETRY

Unit

2

STUDENT WORKBOOK

Book 1

Kendall Hunt |

Lesson 1: Congruent Parts, Part 1

- Let's figure out what the corresponding sides and angles in figures have to do with congruence.

1.1: Notice and Wonder: Transformed Rectangles

What do you notice? What do you wonder?

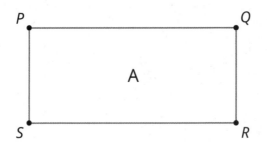

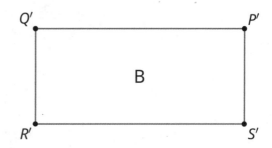

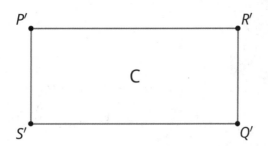

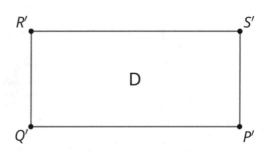

iM KH

1.2: If We Know This, Then We Know That...

Triangle ABC is congruent to triangle DEF.

$\triangle ABC \cong \triangle DEF$

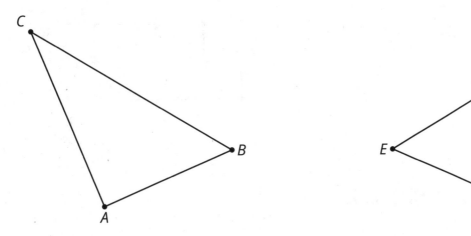

1. Find a sequence of rigid motions that takes triangle ABC to triangle DEF.

2. What is the image of segment BC after that transformation?

3. Explain how you know those segments are congruent.

4. Justify that angle ABC is congruent to angle DEF.

Are you ready for more?

For each figure, draw additional line segments to divide the figure into 2 congruent polygons. Label any new vertices and identify the corresponding vertices of the congruent polygons.

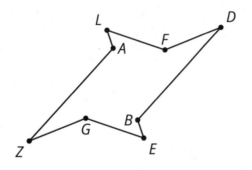

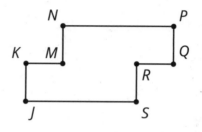

1.3: Making Quadrilaterals

1. Draw a triangle.

2. Find the midpoint of the longest side of your triangle.

3. Rotate your triangle 180° using the midpoint of the longest side as the center of the rotation.

4. Label the **corresponding** parts and mark what must be congruent.

5. Make a conjecture and justify it.
      a. What type of quadrilateral have you formed?

      b. What is the definition of that quadrilateral type?

      c. Why must the quadrilateral you have fit the definition?

Lesson 1 Summary

If a part of the image matches up with a part of the original figure, we call them **corresponding** parts. The part could be an angle, point, or side. We can find corresponding angles, corresponding points, or corresponding sides.

If 2 figures are *not* congruent, then there is *not* a rigid transformation that takes one figure onto the other. If 2 figures are congruent, then there is a rigid transformation that takes one figure onto the other. The same rigid transformation can also be applied to individual parts of the figure, such as segments and angles, because rigid transformations move every point on the plane. Therefore, the corresponding parts of 2 congruent figures are congruent to each other.

Knowing that corresponding parts of congruent figures are congruent can help prove that 2 line segments or 2 angles are congruent, if they are corresponding parts of congruent figures.

Glossary

- corresponding

Lesson 1 Practice Problems

1. When rectangle $ABCD$ is reflected across line EF, the image is $DCBA$. How do you know that segment AB is congruent to segment DC?

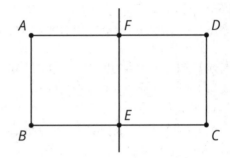

   A. A rectangle has 2 pairs of parallel sides.

   B. Any 2 sides of a rectangle are congruent.

   C. Congruent parts of congruent figures are corresponding.

   D. Corresponding parts of congruent figures are congruent.

2. Triangle FGH is the image of isosceles triangle FEH after a reflection across line HF. Select **all** the statements that are a result of corresponding parts of congruent triangles being congruent.

   $\overline{FE} \cong \overline{HE}$

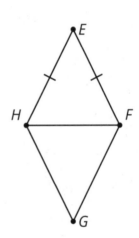

   A. $EFGH$ is a rectangle.

   B. $EFGH$ has 4 congruent sides.

   C. Diagonal FH bisects angles EFG and EHG.

   D. Diagonal FH is perpendicular to side FE.

   E. Angle FEH is congruent to angle FGH.

3. Reflect right triangle ABC across line BC. Classify triangle ACA' according to its side lengths. Explain how you know.

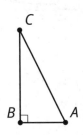

4. Triangles FAD and DCE are translations of triangle ABC

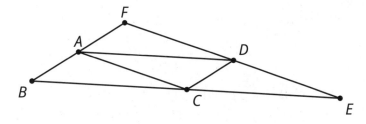

Select **all** the statements that *must* be true.

A. Points B, A, and F are collinear.

B. The measure of angle BCA is the same as the measure of angle CED.

C. Line AD is parallel to line BC.

D. The measure of angle CED is the same as the measure of angle FAD.

E. The measure of angle DAC is the same as the measure of angle BCA.

F. Triangle ADC is a reflection of triangle FAD.

(From Unit 1, Lesson 21.)

5. Triangle *ABC* is congruent to triangles *BAD* and *CEA*.

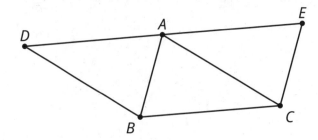

    a. Explain why points *D*, *A*, and *E* are collinear.

    b. Explain why line *DE* is parallel to line *BC*.

(From Unit 1, Lesson 21.)

6.   a. Identify a figure that is the result of a rigid transformation of quadrilateral *ABCD*.

    b. Describe a rigid transformation that would take *ABCD* to that figure.

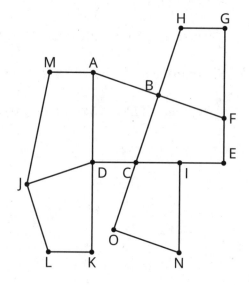

(From Unit 1, Lesson 18.)

iM KH

Lesson 2: Congruent Parts, Part 2

- Let's name figures in ways that help us see the corresponding parts.

2.1: Math Talk: Which Are Congruent?

Each pair of figures is congruent. Decide whether each congruence statement is true or false.

$\triangle ABC \cong \triangle FED$

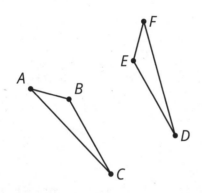

Triangle ABC is congruent to triangle FED.

$PZJM \cong LYXB$

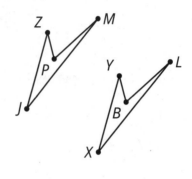

Quadrilateral $PZJM$ is congruent to quadrilateral $LYXB$.

$\triangle JKL \cong \triangle QRS$

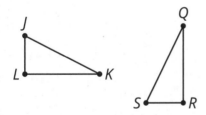

Triangle JKL is congruent to triangle QRS.

$ABCDE \cong PQRST$

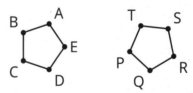

Pentagon $ABCDE$ is congruent to pentagon $PQRST$.

2.2: Which Triangles Are Congruent?

Here are 3 triangles.

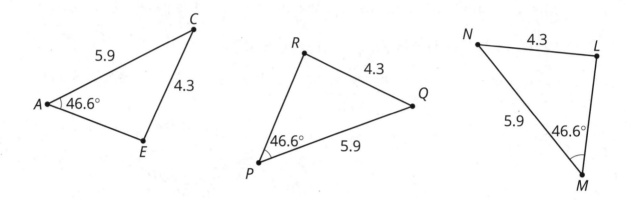

1. Triangle PQR is congruent to which triangle? Explain your reasoning.

2. Show a sequence of rigid motions that takes triangle PQR to that triangle. Draw each step of the transformation.

3. Explain why there can't be a rigid motion from triangle PQR to the other triangle.

2.3: Are These Parts Congruent?

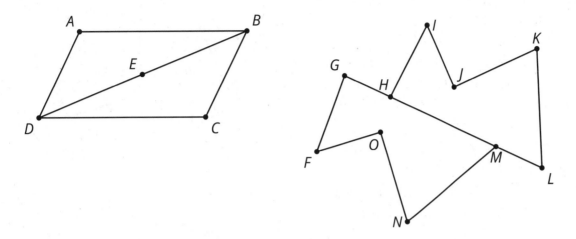

1. Triangle ABD is a rotation of triangle CDB around point E by 180°. Is angle ADB congruent to angle CDB? If so, explain your reasoning. If not, which angle is ADB congruent to?

2. Polygon $HIJKL$ is a reflection and translation of polygon $GFONM$. Is segment KJ congruent to segment NM? If so, explain your reasoning. If not, which segment is NM congruent to?

3. Quadrilateral $PQRS$ is a rotation of polygon $VZYW$. Is angle QRS congruent to angle ZYW? If so, explain your reasoning. If not, which angle is QRS congruent to?

Are you ready for more?

Suppose quadrilateral $PQRS$ was both a rotation of quadrilateral $VZYW$ and also a reflection of quadrilateral $YZVW$. What can we conclude about the shape of our quadrilaterals? Explain why.

Lesson 2 Summary

Naming congruent figures so it's clear from the name which parts correspond makes it easier to check whether 2 figures are congruent and to use corresponding parts. In this image, segment AB appears to be congruent to segment DE. Also, segment EF appears to be congruent to segment BC. So, it makes more sense to conjecture that triangle ABC is congruent to triangle DEF than to conjecture triangle ABC is congruent to triangle FDE.

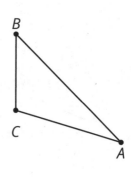

If we are told quadrilateral $MATH$ is congruent to quadrilateral $LOVE$, without even looking at the figures we know:

- Angle M is congruent to angle L.
- Angle A is congruent to angle O.
- Angle T is congruent to angle V.
- Angle H is congruent to angle E.

- Segments MA and LO are congruent.
- Segments AT and OV are congruent.
- Segments TH and VE are congruent.
- Segments HM and EL are congruent.

Quadrilaterals $MATH$ and $LOVE$ can be named in many different ways so that they still correspond—such as $ATHM$ is congruent to $OVEL$ or $THMA$ is congruent to $VELO$. But $ATMH$ is congruent to $LOVE$ means there are different corresponding parts. Note that quadrilateral $MATH$ refers to a different way of connecting the points than quadrilateral $ATMH$.

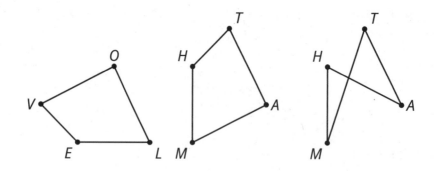

Lesson 2 Practice Problems

1. Line SD is a line of symmetry for figure $AXPDZHMS$. Noah says that $AXPDS$ is congruent to $HMZDS$ because sides AX and HM are corresponding.

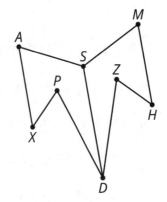

   a. Why is Noah's congruence statement incorrect?

   b. Write a correct congruence statement for the pentagons.

2. FIgure $MBJKGH$ is the image of figure $AFEKJB$ after being rotated 90 degrees counterclockwise about point K. Draw a segment in figure $AFEKJB$ to create a quadrilateral. Draw the image of the segment when rotated 90 degrees counterclockwise about point K.

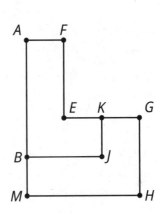

   Write a congruence statement for the quadrilateral you created in figure $AFEKJB$ and the image of the quadrilateral in figure $MBJKGH$.

3. Triangle HEF is the image of triangle FGH after a 180 degree rotation about point K. Select **all** statements that must be true.

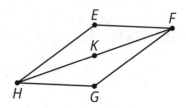

A. Triangle FGH is congruent to triangle FEH.

B. Triangle EFH is congruent to triangle GFH.

C. Angle KHE is congruent to angle KFG.

D. Angle GHK is congruent to angle KHE.

E. Segment EH is congruent to segment FG.

F. Segment GH is congruent to segment EF.

4. When triangle ABC is reflected across line AB, the image is triangle ABD. Why are segment AD and segment AC congruent?

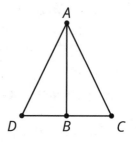

A. Congruent parts of congruent figures are corresponding.

B. Corresponding parts of congruent figures are congruent.

C. An isosceles triangle has a pair of congruent sides.

D. Segment AB is a perpendicular bisector of segment DC.

(From Unit 2, Lesson 1.)

iM KH

5. Elena needs to prove angles BED and BCA are congruent. Provide reasons to support each of her statements.

   a. Line m is parallel to line l.

   b. Angles BED and BCA are congruent.

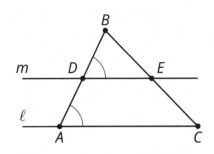

(From Unit 1, Lesson 20.)

6. Triangle FGH is the image of isosceles triangle FEH after a reflection across line HF. Select **all** the statements that are a result of corresponding parts of congruent triangles being congruent.

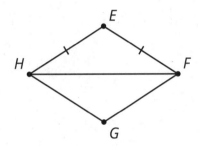

   A. $EFGH$ is a rectangle.

   B. $EFGH$ is a rhombus.

   C. Diagonal FH bisects angles EFG and EHG.

   D. Diagonal FH is perpendicular to side FE.

   E. Angle EHF is congruent to angle FGH.

   F. Angle FEH is congruent to angle FGH.

(From Unit 2, Lesson 1.)

7. This design began from the construction of a regular hexagon.

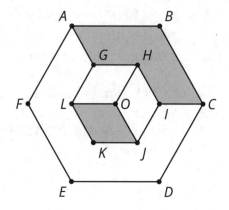

a. Draw 1 segment so the diagram has another hexagon that is congruent to hexagon $ABCIHG$.

b. Explain why the hexagons are congruent.

(From Unit 1, Lesson 22.)

iM KH

Lesson 3: Congruent Triangles, Part 1

- Let's use transformations to be sure that two triangles are congruent.

3.1: True or . . . Sometimes True?: Triangles

If triangle ABC is congruent to triangle $A'B'C'$ . . .

1. What must be true?

2. What could possibly be true?

3. What definitely can't be true?

3.2: Invisible Triangles

Player 1: You are the transformer. Take the transformer card.

Player 2: Select a triangle card. Do not show it to anyone. Study the diagram to figure out which sides and which angles correspond. Tell Player 1 what you have figured out.

Player 1: Take notes about what they tell you so that you know which parts of their triangles correspond. Think of a sequence of rigid motions you could tell your partner to get them to take one of their triangles onto the other. Be specific in your language. The notes on your card can help with this.

Player 2: Listen to the instructions from the transformer. Use tracing paper to follow their instructions. Draw the image after each step. Let them know when they have lined up 1, 2, or all 3 vertices on your triangles.

Are you ready for more?

Replay invisible triangles, but with a twist. This time, the transformer can only use reflections—the last 2 sentence frames on the transformer card. You may wish to include an additional sentence frame: Reflect _____ across the angle bisector of angle _____.

3.3: Why Do They Coincide?

Noah and Priya were playing Invisible Triangles. For card 3, Priya told Noah that in triangles ABC and DEF:

- $\overline{AB} \cong \overline{DE}$

- $\overline{AC} \cong \overline{DF}$

- $\overline{BC} \cong \overline{EF}$

- $\angle A \cong \angle D$

- $\angle B \cong \angle E$

- $\angle C \cong \angle F$

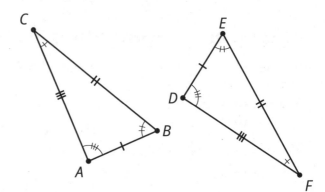

Here are the steps Noah had to tell Priya to do before all 3 vertices coincided:

- Translate triangle ABC by the directed line segment from A to D.

- Rotate the image, triangle $A'B'C'$, using D as the center, so that rays $A''B''$ and DE line up.

- Reflect the image, triangle $A''B''C''$, across line DE.

After those steps, the triangles were lined up perfectly. Now Noah and Priya are working on explaining why their steps worked, and they need some help. Answer their questions.

First, we translate triangle ABC by the directed line segment from A to D. Point A' will coincide with D because we defined our transformation that way. Then, rotate the image, triangle $A'B'C'$, by the angle $B'DE$, so that rays $A''B''$ and DE line up.

1. We know that rays $A''B''$ and DE line up because we said they had to, but why do points B'' and E have to be in the exact same place?

2. Finally, reflect the image, triangle $A''B''C''$ across DE.
   a. How do we know that now, the image of ray $A''C''$ and ray DF will line up?

   b. How do we know that the image of point C'' and point F will line up exactly?

iM KH

Lesson 3 Summary

If all corresponding parts of 2 triangles are congruent, then one triangle can be taken exactly onto the other triangle using a sequence of translations, rotations, and reflections. The congruence of corresponding parts justifies that the vertices of the triangles will line up exactly.

One of the most common ways to line up the vertices is through a translation to get one pair of vertices to line up, followed by a rotation to get a second pair of vertices to line up, and if needed, a reflection to get the third pair of vertices lined up. There are multiple ways to justify why the vertices must line up if the triangles are congruent, but here is one way to do it:

First, translate triangle ABC by the directed line segment from A to D. Points A and D coincide after translating because we defined our translation that way! Then, rotate the image of triangle ABC using D as the center, so that rays $A'B'$ and DE line up.

$\overline{AB} \cong \overline{DE}, \overline{BC} \cong \overline{EF}, \overline{AC} \cong \overline{DF},$
$\angle A \cong \angle D, \angle B \cong \angle E, \angle C \cong \angle F$

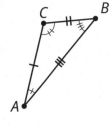
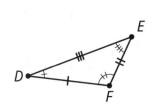

We know that rays $A'B'$ and DE line up because that's how we defined the rotation. The distance AB is the same as the distance DE, because translations and rotations don't change distances. Since points B' and E are the same distance along the same ray from D, they have to be in the same place.

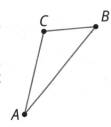
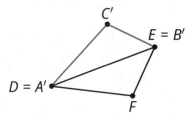

If necessary, reflect triangle $A'B'C'$ across DE so that the image of C is on the same side of DE as F. We know angle A is congruent to angle D because translation, rotation, and reflection don't change angles.

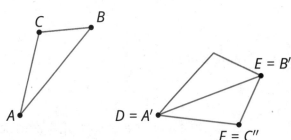

C'' must be on ray DF since both C'' and F are on the same side of DE and make the same angle with it at D. We know the distance AC is the same as the distance DF, so that means C'' is the same distance from A'' as F is from D (because translations and rotations preserve distance). Since F and C'' are the same distance along the same ray from D, they have to be in the same place.

Lesson 3 Practice Problems

1. Triangle ABC is congruent to triangle EDF. So, Kiran knows that there is a sequence of rigid motions that takes ABC to EDF.

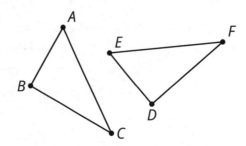

Select **all** true statements after the transformations:

A. Angle A coincides with angle F.

B. Angle B coincides with angle D.

C. Segment AC coincides with segment EF.

D. Segment BC coincides with segment ED.

E. Segment AB coincides with segment ED.

2. A rotation by angle ACE using point C as the center takes triangle CBA onto triangle CDE.

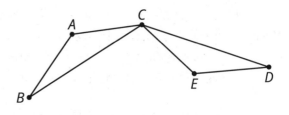

a. Explain why the image of ray CA lines up with ray CE.

b. Explain why the image of A coincides with E.

c. Is triangle CBA congruent to triangle CDE? Explain your reasoning.

iM KH

3. The triangles are congruent. Which sequence of rigid motions will take triangle XYZ onto triangle BCA?

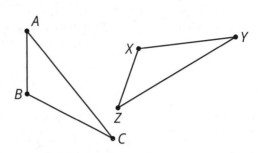

A. Translate XYZ using directed line segment YC. Rotate $X'Y'Z'$ using C as the center so that X' coincides with B. Reflect $X''Y''Z''$ across line CB.

B. Translate XYZ using directed line segment YC. Rotate $X'Y'Z'$ using C as the center so that X' coincides with B. Reflect $X''Y''Z''$ across line AC.

C. Translate XYZ using directed line segment YC. Rotate $X'Y'Z'$ using C as the center so that X' coincides with A. Reflect $X''Y''Z''$ across line CB.

D. Translate XYZ using directed line segment YC. Rotate $X'Y'Z'$ using C as the center so that X' coincides with A. Reflect $X''Y''Z''$ across line AC.

4. Triangle HEF is the image of triangle FGH after a 180 degree rotation around point K. Select **all** statements that must be true.

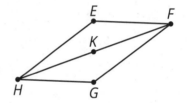

A. Triangle HGF is congruent to triangle FEH.

B. Triangle GFH is congruent to triangle EFH.

C. Angle KHE is congruent to angle KHG.

D. Angle GHK is congruent to angle EFK.

E. Segment EH is congruent to segment GH.

F. Segment HG is congruent to segment FE.

G. Segment FH is congruent to segment HF.

(From Unit 2, Lesson 2.)

5. Line SD is a line of symmetry for figure $ASMHZDPX$. Tyler says that $ASDPX$ is congruent to $SMDZH$ because sides AS and MS are corresponding.

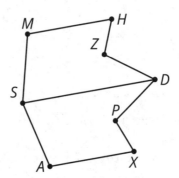

   a. Why is Tyler's congruence statement incorrect?

   b. Write a correct congruence statement for the pentagons.

(From Unit 2, Lesson 2.)

6. Triangle ABC is congruent to triangle DEF. Select **all** the statements that are a result of corresponding parts of congruent triangles being congruent.

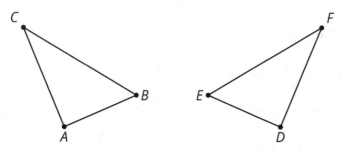

   A. Segment AC is congruent to segment EF.

   B. Segment BC is congruent to segment EF.

   C. Angle BAC is congruent to angle EDF.

   D. Angle BCA is congruent to angle EDF.

   E. Angle CBA is congruent to angle FED.

(From Unit 2, Lesson 1.)

iM KH

7. When triangle ABC is reflected across line AB, the image is triangle ABD. Why is angle ACD congruent to angle ADB?

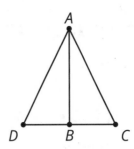

A. Corresponding parts of congruent figures are congruent.

B. Congruent parts of congruent figures are corresponding.

C. Segment AB is a perpendicular bisector of segment DC.

D. An isosceles triangle has a pair of congruent angles.

(From Unit 2, Lesson 1.)

8. Line DE is parallel to line BC.

a. What is the measure of angle EAC?

b. What is the measure of angle DAB?

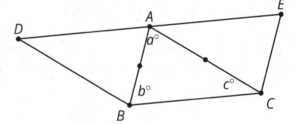

(From Unit 1, Lesson 21.)

Lesson 4: Congruent Triangles, Part 2

- Let's figure out if there are shortcuts for being sure two triangles are congruent.

4.1: Make That Triangle

Draw triangle ABC with these measurements:

- Angle A is 40 degrees.

- Angle B is 20 degrees.

- Angle C is 120 degrees.

- Segment AB is 5 centimeters.

- Segment AC is 2 centimeters.

- Segment BC is 3.7 centimeters.

Highlight each piece of given information that you used. Check your triangle to make sure the remaining measurements match.

4.2: Info Gap: Too Much Information

Your teacher will give you either a problem card or a data card. Do not show or read your card to your partner.

If your teacher gives you the data card:

1. Silently read the information on your card.

2. Ask your partner "What specific information do you need?" and wait for your partner to ask for information. Only give information that is on your card. (Do not figure out anything for your partner!)

3. Before telling your partner the information, ask "Why do you need to know (that piece of information)?"

4. Read the problem card, and solve the problem independently.

5. Share the data card, and discuss your reasoning.

If your teacher gives you the problem card:

1. Silently read your card and think about what information you need to answer the question.

2. Ask your partner for the specific information that you need.

3. Explain to your partner how you are using the information to solve the problem.

4. When you have enough information, share the problem card with your partner, and solve the problem independently.

5. Read the data card, and discuss your reasoning.

Are you ready for more?

Elena wonders whether she could play the Info Gap with area included as an extra piece of information in the data cards. She draws a card with this information and asks Han to play.

1. If Han asks for 2 sides and the area, do you think this will be enough information for Han to draw a congruent triangle?

2. If Han asks for 2 angles and the area, do you think this will be enough information for Han to draw a congruent triangle?

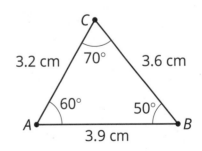

Area = 5.4 cm^2

4.3: Too Little Information?

Jada and Tyler were playing the Info Gap, using Card 3.

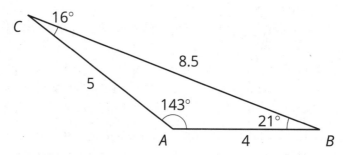

Tyler asked, "Can I have 2 sides and an angle?"

Jada told Tyler that one angle was 16°, one side was 5 cm, and one side was 4 cm. Here is the triangle Tyler made:

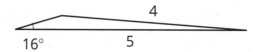

1. Is Tyler's triangle congruent to the triangle on the Data Card?

2. Did Tyler do anything that didn't match Jada's instructions?

3. How could Tyler have made a more specific request for 2 sides and an angle so that his triangle was guaranteed to match Jada's?

iM KH

Lesson 4 Summary

If we know that every pair of corresponding parts is congruent, then we know the 2 triangles are congruent. But we don't need that much information. If we know the angles of a triangle are 30 degrees and 60 degrees, we can figure out the third angle is 90 degrees. So when we start drawing a triangle, the triangle is complete before we measure every angle. Figuring out which sets of measurements are enough to draw a complete triangle tells us which sets of measurements are enough to prove triangles are congruent. Here are 3 sets of measurements that appear to be enough information to prove that the 2 triangles will be congruent:

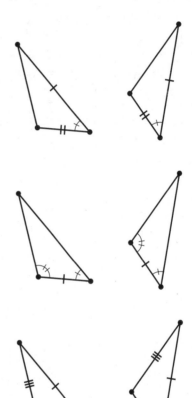

- Two pairs of corresponding sides are congruent and the angles between those sides are congruent.

- Two pairs of corresponding angles are congruent and the sides between those angles are congruent.

- Three pairs of corresponding sides are congruent.

Lesson 4 Practice Problems

1. Match each statement using only the information shown in the pairs of congruent triangles.

   A. In the 2 triangles there are 3 pairs of congruent sides.

   B. The 2 sides and the included angle of one triangle are congruent to 2 sides and the included angle of another triangle.

   C. The 2 angles and the included side of one triangle are congruent to 2 angles and the included side of another triangle.

   1.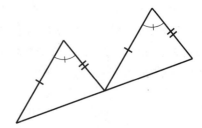

   2.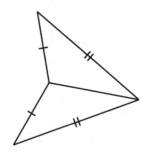

   3.

2. Sketch the unique triangles that can be made with angle measures 40° and 100° and side length 3. How do you know you have sketched all possibilities?

iM KH

3. What is the least amount of information that you need to construct a triangle congruent to this one?

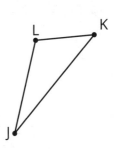

4. Triangle ABC is congruent to triangle EDF. So, Mai knows that there is a sequence of rigid motions that takes ABC to EDF.

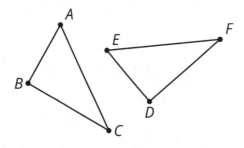

Select **all** true statements after the transformations:

A. Angle A coincides with angle E.

B. Angle B coincides with angle F.

C. Segment AB coincides with segment EF.

D. Segment BC coincides with segment DF.

E. Segment AC coincides with segment ED.

(From Unit 2, Lesson 3.)

5. A rotation by angle ACE using point C as the center takes triangle CBA onto triangle CDE.

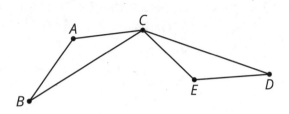

   a. Explain why the image of segment CB lines up with segment CD.

   b. Explain why the image of B coincides with D.

   c. Is triangle ABC congruent to triangle EDC? Explain your reasoning.

   (From Unit 2, Lesson 3.)

6. Line EF is a line of symmetry for figure $ABECDF$. Clare says that $ABEF$ is congruent to $CDFE$ because sides AB and CD are corresponding.

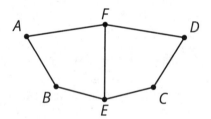

   a. Why is Clare's congruence statement incorrect?

   b. Write a correct congruence statement for the quadrilaterals.

   (From Unit 2, Lesson 2.)

7. Triangle HEF is the image of triangle HGF after a reflection across line FH. Select **all** statements that must be true.

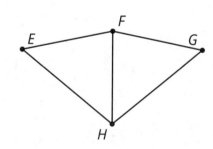

iM KH

A. Triangle FGH is congruent to triangle FEH.

B. Triangle EFH is congruent to triangle GFH.

C. Angle HFE is congruent to angle FHG.

D. Angle EFG is congruent to angle EHG.

E. Segment EH is congruent to segment FG.

F. Segment GH is congruent to segment EH.

(From Unit 2, Lesson 2.)

8. When rectangle $ABCD$ is reflected across line EF, the image is $BADC$. How do you know that segment AD is congruent to segment BC?

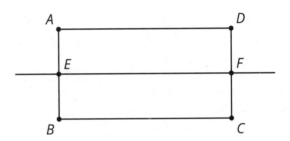

A. A rectangle has 2 pairs of parallel sides.

B. Any 2 sides of a rectangle are congruent.

C. Corresponding parts of congruent figures are congruent.

D. Congruent parts of congruent figures are corresponding.

(From Unit 2, Lesson 1.)

9. This design began from the construction of a regular hexagon. Describe a rigid motion that will take the figure onto itself.

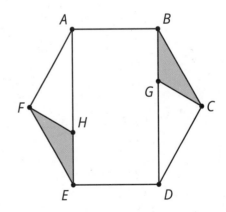

(From Unit 1, Lesson 22.)

Lesson 5: Points, Segments, and Zigzags

- Let's figure out when segments are congruent.

5.1: What's the Point?

If A is a point on the plane and B is a point on the plane, then A is congruent to B.

Try to prove this claim by explaining why you can be certain the claim must be true, or try to disprove this claim by explaining why the claim cannot be true. If you can find a counterexample in which the "if" part (hypothesis) is true, but the "then" part (conclusion) is false, you have disproved the claim.

5.2: What's the Segment?

Prove the conjecture: If AB is a segment in the plane and CD is a segment in the plane with the same length as AB, then AB is congruent to CD.

Are you ready for more?

Prove or disprove the following claim: "If EF is a piece of string in the plane, and GH is a piece of string in the plane with the same length as EF, then EF is congruent to GH."

5.3: Zig Then Zag

$\overline{QR} \cong \overline{XY}, \overline{RS} \cong \overline{YZ}, \angle R \cong \angle Y$

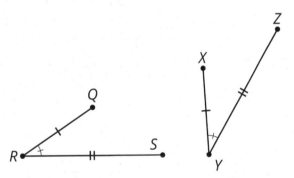

1. Here are some statements about 2 zigzags. Put them in order to write a proof about figures QRS and XYZ.

   ○ 1: Therefore, figure QRS is congruent to figure XYZ.

   ○ 2: S' must be on ray YZ since both S' and Z are on the same side of XY and make the same angle with it at Y.

   ○ 3: Segments QR and XY are the same length, so they are congruent. Therefore, there is a rigid motion that takes QR to XY. Apply that rigid motion to figure QRS.

   ○ 4: Since points S' and Z are the same distance along the same ray from Y, they have to be in the same place.

   ○ 5: If necessary, reflect the image of figure QRS across XY to be sure the image of S, which we will call S', is on the same side of XY as Z.

2. Take turns with your partner stating steps in the proof that figure $ABCD$ is congruent to figure $EFGH$.

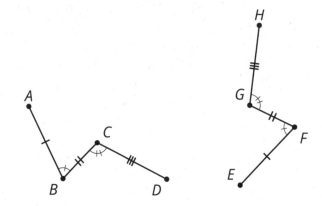

Lesson 5 Summary

If 2 figures are congruent, then there is a sequence of rigid motions that takes one figure onto the other. We can use this fact to prove that any point is congruent to another point. We can also prove segments of the same length are congruent. Finally, we can put together arguments to prove entire figures are congruent.

These statements prove ABC is congruent to XYZ.

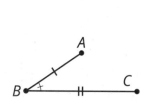
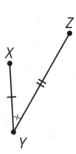

- Segments AB and XY are the same length, so they are congruent. Therefore, there is a rigid motion that takes AB to XY. Apply that rigid motion to figure ABC.

- If necessary, reflect the image of figure ABC across XY to be sure the image of C, which we will call C', is on the same side of XY as Z.

- C' must be on ray YZ since both C' and Z are on the same side of XY and make the same angle with it at Y.

- Since points C' and Z are the same distance along the same ray from Y, they have to be in the same place.

- Therefore, figure ABC is congruent to figure XYZ.

iM KH

Lesson 5 Practice Problems

1. Write a sequence of rigid motions to take figure ABC to figure DEF.

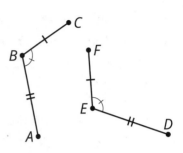

2. Prove the circle centered at A is congruent to the circle centered at C.

   $AB = CD$

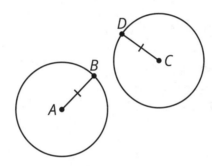

3. Which conjecture is possible to prove?

   A. All quadrilaterals with at least one side length of 3 are congruent.

   B. All rectangles with at least one side length of 3 are congruent.

   C. All rhombuses with at least one side length of 3 are congruent.

   D. All squares with at least one side length of 3 are congruent.

4. Match each statement using only the information shown in the pairs of congruent triangles.

    A. The 2 sides and the included angle of one triangle are congruent to 2 sides and the included angle of another triangle.

    B. The 2 angles and the included side of one triangle are congruent to 2 angles and the included side of another triangle.

    1.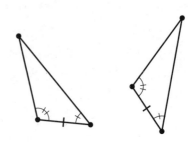

    C. In the 2 triangles there are 3 pairs of congruent sides.

    2.

    3.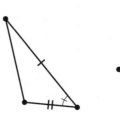

(From Unit 2, Lesson 4.)

5. Triangle HEF is the image of triangle HGF after a reflection across line FH. Write a congruence statement for the 2 congruent triangles.

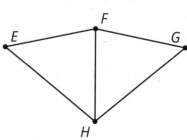

(From Unit 2, Lesson 2.)

6. Triangle ABC is congruent to triangle EDF. So, Lin knows that there is a sequence of rigid motions that takes ABC to EDF.

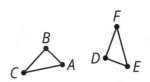

Select **all** true statements after the transformations:

    A. Angle A coincides with angle F.

    B. Angle B coincides with angle D.

    C. Angle C coincides with angle E.

    D. Segment BA coincides with segment DE.

    E. Segment BC coincides with segment FE.

(From Unit 2, Lesson 3.)

7. This design began from the construction of a regular hexagon. Is quadrilateral $JKLO$ congruent to the other 2 quadrilaterals? Explain how you know.

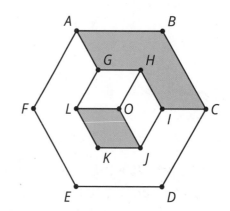

(From Unit 1, Lesson 22.)

Lesson 6: Side-Angle-Side Triangle Congruence

- Let's use definitions and theorems to figure out what must be true about shapes, without having to measure all parts of the shapes.

6.1: Information Overload?

Highlight each piece of given information that is used in the proof, and each line in the proof where that piece of information is used.

Given:

- $\overline{AB} \cong \overline{DE}$

- $\overline{AC} \cong \overline{DF}$

- $\overline{BC} \cong \overline{EF}$

- $\angle A \cong \angle D$

- $\angle B \cong \angle E$

- $\angle C \cong \angle F$

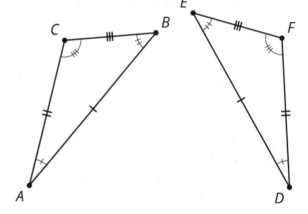

Proof:

1. Segments AB and DE are the same length so they are congruent. Therefore, there is a rigid motion that takes AB to DE.

2. Apply that rigid motion to triangle ABC. The image of A will coincide with D, and the image of B will coincide with E.

3. We cannot be sure that the image of C coincides with F yet. If necessary, reflect the image of triangle ABC across DE to be sure the image of C, which we will call C', is on the same side of DE as F. (This reflection does not change the image of A or B.)

4. We know the image of angle A is congruent to angle D because rigid motions don't change the size of angles.

5. C' must be on ray DF since both C' and F are on the same side of DE, and make the same angle with it at D.

iM KH

6. Segment DC' is the image of AC and rigid motions preserve distance, so they must have the same length.

7. We also know AC has the same length as DF. So DC' and DF must be the same length.

8. Since C' and F are the same distance along the same ray from D, they have to be in the same place.

9. We have shown that a rigid motion takes A to D, B to E, and C to F; therefore, triangle ABC is congruent to triangle DEF.

6.2: Proving the Side-Angle-Side Triangle Congruence Theorem

1. Two triangles have 2 pairs of corresponding sides congruent, and the corresponding angles between those sides are congruent. Sketch 2 triangles that fit this description and label them LMN and PQR, so that:
   - Segment LM is congruent to segment PQ
   - Segment LN is congruent to segment PR
   - Angle L is congruent to angle P

2. Use a sequence of rigid motions to take LMN onto PQR. For each step, explain how you know that one or more vertices will line up.

3. Look back at the congruent triangle proofs you've read and written. Do you have enough information here to use a proof that is like one you saw earlier? Use one of those proofs to guide you in writing a proof for this situation.

Are you ready for more?

It follows from the Side-Angle-Side Triangle Congruence Theorem that if the lengths of 2 sides of a triangle are known, and the measure of the angle between those 2 sides is known, there can only be one possible length for the third side.

Suppose a triangle has sides of lengths of 5 cm and 12 cm.

1. What is the longest the third side could be? What is the shortest it could be?

2. How long would the third side be if the angle between the two sides measured 90 degrees?

6.3: What Do We Know For Sure About Isosceles Triangles?

Mai and Kiran want to prove that in an isosceles triangle, the 2 base angles are congruent. Finish the proof that they started. Draw the **auxiliary line** and define it so that you can use the Side-Angle-Side Triangle Congruence Theorem to complete each statement in the proof.

Draw _____.

Segment PA is congruent to segment PB because of the definition of isosceles triangle.

Angle _____ is congruent to angle _____ because _____.

Segment PQ is congruent to itself.

Therefore, triangle APQ is congruent to triangle BPQ by the Side-Angle-Side Triangle Congruence Theorem.

Therefore, _____.

Lesson 6 Summary

If all pairs of corresponding sides and angles in 2 triangles are congruent, then it is possible to find a rigid transformation that takes corresponding vertices onto one another. This proves that if 2 triangles have all pairs of corresponding sides and angles congruent, then the triangles must be congruent. But, justifying that the vertices must line up does not require knowing all the pairs of corresponding sides and angles are congruent. We can justify that the triangles must be congruent if all we know is that 2 pairs of corresponding sides and the pair of corresponding angles between the sides are congruent. This is called the *Side-Angle-Side Triangle Congruence Theorem*.

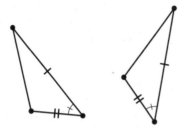

To find out if 2 triangles, or 2 parts of triangles, are congruent, see if the given information or the diagram indicates that 2 pairs of corresponding sides and the pair of corresponding angles between the sides are congruent. If that is the case, we don't need to show and justify all the transformations that take one triangle onto the other triangle. Instead, we can explain how we know the pairs of corresponding sides and angles are congruent and say that the 2 triangles must be congruent because of the Side-Angle-Side Triangle Congruence Theorem.

Sometimes, to find congruent triangles, we may need to add more lines to the diagram. We can decide what properties those lines have based on how we construct the lines (An angle bisector? A perpendicular bisector? A line connecting 2 given points?). Mathematicians call these additional lines **auxiliary lines** because auxiliary means "providing additional help or support." These are lines that give us extra help in seeing hidden triangle structures.

Glossary

- auxiliary line

Lesson 6 Practice Problems

1. Triangle DAC is isosceles with congruent sides AD and AC. Which additional given information is sufficient for showing that triangle DBC is isosceles? Select **all** that apply.

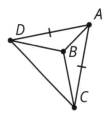

A. Line AB is an angle bisector of DAC.

B. Angle BAD is congruent to angle ABC.

C. Angle BDC is congruent to angle BCD.

D. Angle ABD is congruent to angle ABC.

E. Triangle DAB is congruent to triangle CAB.

2. Tyler has written an incorrect proof to show that quadrilateral $ABCD$ is a parallelogram. He knows segments AB and DC are congruent. He also knows angles ABC and ADC are congruent. Find the mistake in his proof.

Segment AC is congruent to itself, so triangle ABC is congruent to triangle ADC by Side-Angle-Side Triangle Congruence Theorem. Since the triangles are congruent, so are the corresponding parts, and so angle DAC is congruent to ACB. In quadrilateral $ABCD$, AB is congruent to CD and AD is parallel to CB. Since AD is parallel to CB, alternate interior angles DAC and BCA are congruent. Since alternate interior angles are congruent, AB must be parallel to CD. Quadrilateral $ABCD$ must be a parallelogram since both pairs of opposite sides are parallel.

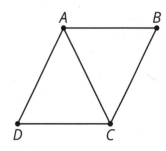

3. Triangles ACD and BCD are isosceles. Angle BAC has a measure of 18 degrees and angle BDC has a measure of 48 degrees. Find the measure of angle ABD.

$\overline{AD} \cong \overline{AC}$ and $\overline{BD} \cong \overline{BC}$

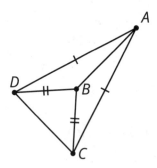

4. Here are some statements about 2 zigzags. Put them in order to prove figure ABC is congruent to figure DEF.

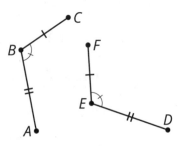

- 1: If necessary, reflect the image of figure ABC across DE to be sure the image of C, which we will call C', is on the same side of DE as F.

- 2: C' must be on ray EF since both C' and F are on the same side of DE and make the same angle with it at E.

- 3: Segments AB and DE are the same length so they are congruent. Therefore, there is a rigid motion that takes AB to DE. Apply that rigid motion to figure ABC.

- 4: Since points C' and F are the same distance along the same ray from E they have to be in the same place.

- 5: Therefore, figure ABC is congruent to figure DEF.

(From Unit 2, Lesson 5.)

iM KH

5. Match each statement using only the information shown in the pairs of congruent triangles.

   A. The 2 angles and the included side of one triangle are congruent to 2 angles and the included side of another triangle.

   B. In the 2 triangles there are 3 pairs of congruent sides.

   C. The 2 sides and the included angle of one triangle are congruent to 2 sides and the included angle of another triangle.

1.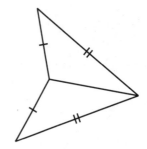

2.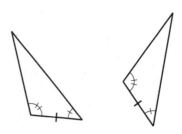

3.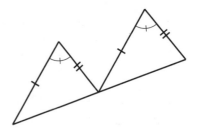

(From Unit 2, Lesson 4.)

6. Triangle ABC is congruent to triangle EDF. So, Priya knows that there is a sequence of rigid motions that takes ABC to EDF.

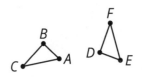

   Select **all** true statements after the transformations:

A. Segment AB coincides with segment EF.

B. Segment BC coincides with segment DF.

C. Segment AC coincides with segment ED.

D. Angle A coincides with angle E.

E. Angle C coincides with angle F.

(From Unit 2, Lesson 3.)

Lesson 7: Angle-Side-Angle Triangle Congruence

- Let's see if we can prove other sets of measurements that guarantee triangles are congruent, and apply those theorems.

7.1: Notice and Wonder: Assertion

Assertion: Through 2 distinct points passes a unique line. Two lines are said to be *distinct* if there is at least 1 point that belongs to one but not the other. Otherwise, we say the lines are the same. Lines that have no point in common are said to be *parallel*.

Therefore, we can conclude: given 2 distinct lines, either they are parallel, or they have exactly 1 point in common.

What do you notice? What do you wonder?

7.2: Proving the Angle-Side-Angle Triangle Congruence Theorem

1. Two triangles have 2 pairs of corresponding angles congruent, and the corresponding sides between those angles are congruent. Sketch 2 triangles that fit this description.

2. Label the triangles WXY and DEF, so that angle W is congruent to angle D, angle X is congruent to angle E, and side WX is congruent to side DE.

3. Use a sequence of rigid motions to take triangle WXY onto triangle DEF. For each step, explain how you know that one or more vertices will line up.

7.3: Find the Missing Angle Measures

Lines ℓ and m are parallel. $a = 42$. Find b, c, d, e, f, g, and h.

$\ell \parallel m$

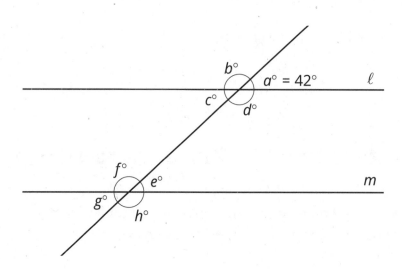

iM KH

7.4: What Do We Know For Sure About Parallelograms?

Quadrilateral $ABCD$ is a **parallelogram**. By definition, that means that segment AB is parallel to segment CD, and segment BC is parallel to segment AD.

1. Sketch parallelogram $ABCD$ and then draw an auxiliary line to show how $ABCD$ can be decomposed into 2 triangles.

2. Prove that the 2 triangles you created are congruent, and explain why that shows one pair of opposite sides of a parallelogram must be congruent.

Are you ready for more?

When we have 3 consecutive vertices of a polygon A, B, and C so that the triangle ABC lies entirely inside the polygon, we call B an *ear* of the polygon.

1. How many ears does a parallelogram have?

2. Draw a quadrilateral that has fewer ears than a parallelogram.

3. In 1975, Gary Meisters proved that every polygon has at least 2 ears. Draw a hexagon with only 2 ears.

Lesson 7 Summary

We know that in 2 triangles, if 2 pairs of corresponding sides and the pair of corresponding angles between the sides are congruent, then the triangles must be congruent. But we don't always know that 2 pairs of corresponding sides are congruent. For example, when proving that opposite sides are congruent in any parallelogram, we only have information about 1 pair of corresponding sides. That is why we need other ways than the Side-Angle-Side Triangle Congruence Theorem to prove triangles are congruent.

In 2 triangles, if 2 pairs of corresponding angles and the pair of corresponding sides between the angles are congruent, then the triangles must be congruent. This is called the *Angle-Side-Angle Triangle Congruence Theorem*.

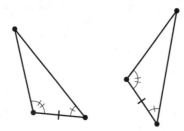

When proving that 2 triangles are congruent, look at the diagram and given information and think about whether it will be easier to find 2 pairs of corresponding angles that are congruent or 2 pairs of corresponding sides that are congruent. Then check if there is enough information to use the Angle-Side-Angle Triangle Congruence Theorem or the Side-Angle-Side Triangle Congruence Theorem.

The Angle-Side-Angle Triangle Congruence Theorem can be used to prove that, in a **parallelogram**, opposite sides are congruent. A parallelogram is defined to be a quadrilateral with 2 pairs of opposite sides parallel.

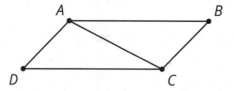

We could prove that triangles ABC and CDA are congruent by the Angle-Side-Angle Triangle Congruence Theorem. Then we can say segment AD is congruent to segment CB because they are corresponding parts of congruent triangles.

Glossary
- parallelogram

Lesson 7 Practice Problems

1. What triangle congruence theorem could you use to prove triangle ADE is congruent to triangle CBE?

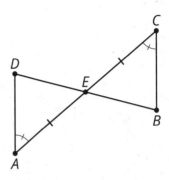

2. Han wrote a proof that triangle BCD is congruent to triangle DAB. Han's proof is incomplete. How can Han fix his proof?

$DC \parallel AB$

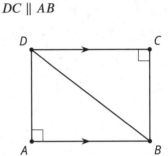

- ○ Line AB is parallel to line DC and cut by transversal DB. So angles CDB and ABD are alternate interior angles and must be congruent.

- ○ Side DB is congruent to side BD because they're the same segment.

- ○ Angle A is congruent to angle C because they're both right angles.

- ○ By the Angle-Side-Angle Triangle Congruence Theorem, triangle BCD is congruent to triangle DAB.

3. Segment GE is an angle bisector of both angle HEF and angle FGH. Prove triangle HGE is congruent to triangle FGE.

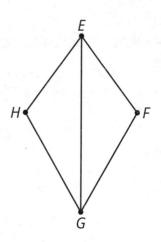

4. Triangles ACD and BCD are isosceles. Angle BAC has a measure of 33 degrees and angle BDC has a measure of 35 degrees. Find the measure of angle ABD.

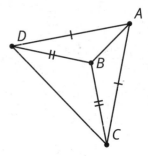

(From Unit 2, Lesson 6.)

5. Which conjecture is possible to prove?

    A. All triangles with at least one side length of 5 are congruent.

    B. All pentagons with at least one side length of 5 are congruent.

    C. All rectangles with at least one side length of 5 are congruent.

    D. All squares with at least one side length of 5 are congruent.

(From Unit 2, Lesson 5.)

iM KH

6. Andre is drawing a triangle that is congruent to this one. He begins by constructing an angle congruent to angle *LKJ*. What is the least amount of additional information that Andre needs to construct a triangle congruent to this one?

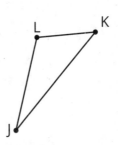

(From Unit 2, Lesson 4.)

7. Here is a diagram of a straightedge and compass construction. *C* is the center of one circle, and *B* is the center of the other. Which segment has the same length as segment *CA*?

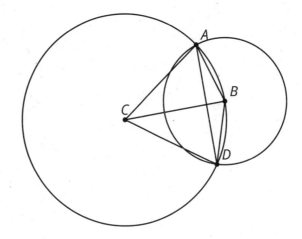

A. *BA*

B. *BD*

C. *CB*

D. *AD*

(From Unit 1, Lesson 1.)

Lesson 8: The Perpendicular Bisector Theorem

- Let's convince ourselves that what we've conjectured about perpendicular bisectors must be true.

8.1: Which One Doesn't Belong: Intersecting Lines

Which one doesn't belong?

A

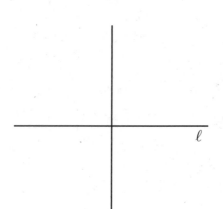

B

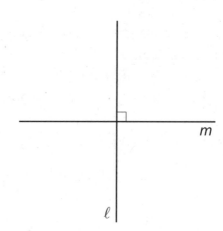

C

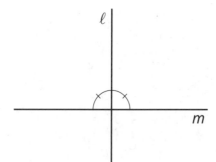

D

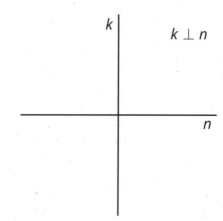

iM KH

8.2: Lots of Lines

Diego, Jada, and Noah were given the following task:

Prove that if a point C is the same distance from A as it is from B, then C must be on the perpendicular bisector of AB.

At first they were really stuck. Noah asked, "How do you prove a point is on a line?" Their teacher gave them the hint, "Another way to think about it is to draw a line that you know C is on, and prove that line has to be the perpendicular bisector."

They each drew a line and thought about their pictures. Here are their rough drafts.

Diego's approach: "I drew a line through C that was perpendicular to AB and through the midpoint of AB. That line is the perpendicular bisector of AB and C is on it, so that proves C is on the perpendicular bisector."

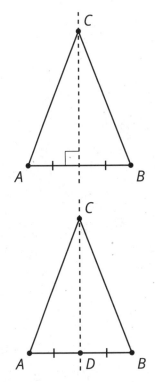

Jada's approach: "I thought the line through C would probably go through the midpoint of AB so I drew that and labeled the midpoint D. Triangle ACB is isosceles, so angles A and B are congruent, and AC and BC are congruent. And AD and DB are congruent because D is a midpoint. That made two congruent triangles by the Side-Angle-Side Triangle Congruence Theorem. So I know angle ADC and angle BDC are congruent, but I still don't know if DC is the perpendicular bisector of AB."

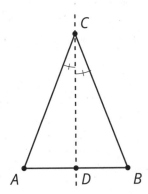

Noah's approach: "In the Isosceles Triangle Theorem proof, Mai and Kiran drew an angle bisector in their isosceles triangle, so I'll try that. I'll draw the angle bisector of angle ACB. The point where the angle bisector hits AB will be D. So triangles ACD and BCD are congruent, which means AD and BD are congruent, so D is a midpoint and CD is the perpendicular bisector."

1. With your partner, discuss each student's approach.
   ○ What do you notice that this student understands about the problem?

   ○ What question would you ask them to help them move forward?

2. Using the ideas you heard and the ways you think each student could make their explanation better, write your own explanation for why C must be on the perpendicular bisector of A and B.

Are you ready for more?

Elena has another approach: "I drew the line of reflection. If you reflect across C, then A and B will switch places, meaning A' coincides with B, and B' coincides with A. C will stay in its place, so the triangles will be congruent."

1. What feedback would you give Elena?

2. Write your own explanation based on Elena's idea.

iM KH

8.3: Not Too Close, Not Too Far

1. Work on your own to make a diagram and write a rough draft of a proof for the statement:
   If P is a point on the perpendicular bisector of AB, prove that the distance from P to A is the same as the distance from P to B.

2. With your partner, discuss each other's drafts. Record your partner's feedback for your proof.
   ◦ What do you notice that your partner understands about the problem?

   ◦ What question would you ask them to help them move forward?

Lesson 8 Summary

The perpendicular bisector of a line segment is exactly those points that are the same distance from both endpoints of the line segment. This idea can be broken down into 2 statements:

- If a point is on the perpendicular bisector of a segment, then it must be the same distance from both endpoints of the line segment.

- If a point is the same distance from both endpoints of a line segment, then it must be on the perpendicular bisector of the segment.

These statements are **converses** of one another. Two statements are converses if the "if" part and the "then" part are swapped. The converse of a true statement isn't always true, but in this case, both statements are true parts of the Perpendicular Bisector Theorem.

A line of reflection is the perpendicular bisector of segments connecting points in the original figure with corresponding points in the image. Therefore, these 3 lines are all the same:

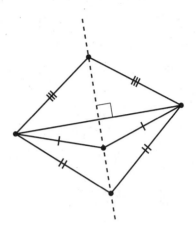

- The perpendicular bisector of a segment.

- The set of points equidistant from the 2 endpoints of a segment.

- The line of reflection that takes the 2 endpoints of the segment onto each other, and the segment onto itself.

It is useful to know that the perpendicular bisector of a line segment is also all the points which are the same distance from both endpoints of the line segment, because then:

- If 2 points are both equidistant from the endpoints of a segment, then the line through those points must be the perpendicular bisector of the segment (because 2 points define a unique line).

- If 2 points are both equidistant from the endpoints of a segment, then the line through those must be the line of reflection that takes the segment to itself and swaps the endpoints.

- If a point is on the line of reflection, then it is the same distance from that point to a point in the original figure and to its corresponding point in the image.

- If a point is on the perpendicular bisector of a segment, then it is the same distance from that point to both endpoints of the segment.

Glossary

- converse

Lesson 8 Practice Problems

1. Each statement is always true. Select **all** statements for which the converse is also always true.

   A. Statement: If 2 angles are vertical, then they are congruent. Converse: If 2 angles are congruent, then they are vertical.

   B. Statement: If 2 lines are perpendicular, then they intersect to form 4 right angles. Converse: If 2 lines intersect to form 4 right angles, then they are perpendicular.

   C. Statement: If a point is equidistant from the 2 endpoints of a segment, then it lies on the perpendicular bisector of the segment. Converse: If a point lies on the perpendicular bisector of a segment, then it is equidistant from the 2 endpoints of the segment.

   D. Statement: In an isosceles triangle, the base angles are congruent. Converse: If the base angles of a triangle are congruent, then the triangle is isosceles.

   E. Statement: If 2 angles form a straight angle, then they are supplementary. Converse: If 2 angles are supplementary, then they form a straight angle.

2. In isosceles triangle DAC, AD is congruent to AC. Kiran knows that the base angles of an isosceles triangle are congruent. What additional information does Kiran need to know in order to show that AB is a perpendicular bisector of segment CD?

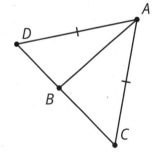

3. Han and Priya were making a kite. Han cut out a piece of fabric so that there were 2 short sides of the same length on top and 2 long sides of the same length on the bottom. Priya cut 2 pieces of wood to go across the diagonals of the kite. They attached the wood like this:

Han asked Priya to measure the angle to make sure the pieces of wood were perpendicular. Priya said, "If we were careful about the lengths of the sides of the fabric, we don't need to measure the angle. It has to be a right angle."

Complete Priya's explanation to Han.

4. Prove triangle ADE is congruent to triangle CBE. $\angle A \cong \angle C, \overline{AE} \cong \overline{CE}$

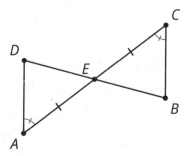

(From Unit 2, Lesson 7.)

5. Triangle DAC is isosceles. What information do you need to show that triangle DBA is congruent to triangle CBA by the Side-Angle-Side Triangle Congruence Theorem?

$$\overline{AD} \cong \overline{AC}$$

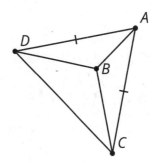

(From Unit 2, Lesson 6.)

6. Write a sequence of rigid motions to take figure CBA to figure MLK.

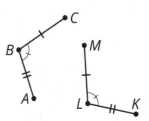

(From Unit 2, Lesson 5.)

7. Here is a quadrilateral inscribed in a circle.

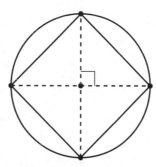

Jada says that it is square because folding it along the horizontal dashed line and then the vertical dashed line gives 4 congruent sides. Do you agree with Jada?

(From Unit 1, Lesson 7.)

Lesson 9: Side-Side-Side Triangle Congruence

- Let's see if we can prove one more set of conditions that guarantee triangles are congruent, and apply theorems.

9.1: Dare to Be Different

Construct a triangle with the given side lengths on tracing paper.

_____

_____

_____

Can you make a triangle that doesn't look like anyone else's?

9.2: Proving the Side-Side-Side Triangle Congruence Theorem

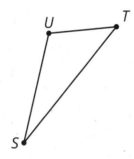
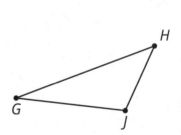

Priya was given this task to complete:

Use a sequence of rigid motions to take STU onto GHJ. Given that segment ST is congruent to segment GH, segment TU is congruent to segment HJ, and segment SU is congruent to segment GJ. For each step, explain how you know that one or more vertices will line up.

Help her finish the missing steps in her proof:

1. ST is the same length as _____, so they are congruent. Therefore, there is a rigid motion that takes ST to _____.

iM KH

2. Apply this rigid motion to triangle STU. The image of T will coincide with _____ , and the image of S will coincide with _____ .

3. We cannot be sure that the image of U, which we will call U', coincides with _____ yet. If it does, then our rigid motion takes STU to GHJ, proving that triangle STU is congruent to triangle GHJ. If it does not, then we continue as follows.

4. HJ is congruent to the image of _____ , because rigid motions preserve distance.

5. Therefore, H is equidistant from U' and _____ .

6. A similar argument shows that G is equidistant from U' and _____ .

7. GH is the _____ of the segment connecting U' and J, because the _____ is determined by 2 points that are both equidistant from the endpoints of a segment.

8. Reflection across the _____ of $U'J$, takes _____ to _____ .

9. Therefore, after the reflection, all 3 pairs of vertices coincide, proving triangles _____ and _____ are congruent.

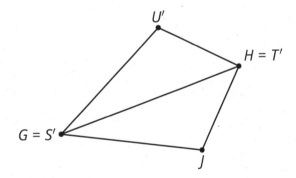

Now, help Priya by finishing a few-sentence summary of her proof. "To prove 2 triangles must be congruent if all 3 pairs of corresponding sides are congruent . . . ."

Are you ready for more?

It follows from the Side-Side-Side Triangle Congruence Theorem that, if the lengths of 3 sides of a triangle are known, then the measures of all the angles must also be determined. Suppose a triangle has two sides of length 4 cm.

1. Use a ruler and protractor to make triangles and find the measure of the angle between those sides if the third side has these other measurements.

Side Length of Third Side	Angle Between First Two Sides
1 cm	
2 cm	
3 cm	
4 cm	
5 cm	
6 cm	
7 cm	

2. Do the side length and angle measures exhibit a linear relationship?

9.3: What Else Do We Know For Sure About Parallelograms?

Quadrilateral $ABCD$ is a parallelogram. By definition, that means that segment AB is parallel to segment CD, and segment BC is parallel to segment AD.

Prove that angle B is congruent to angle D.

1. Work on your own to make a diagram and write a rough draft of a proof.

2. With your partner, discuss each other's drafts.
   ○ What do you notice your partner understands about the problem?

   ○ What revision would help them move forward?

3. Work together to revise your drafts into a clear proof that everyone in your class could follow and agree with.

Lesson 9 Summary

So far, we've learned the Side-Angle-Side and Angle-Side-Angle Triangle Congruence Theorems. Sometimes, we don't have any information about corresponding pairs of angle measures in triangles. In this case, use the *Side-Side-Side Triangle Congruence Theorem*: In 2 triangles, if all 3 pairs of corresponding sides are congruent, then the triangles must be congruent.

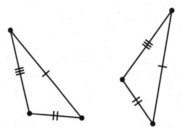

To prove that 2 triangles are congruent, look at the diagram and given information and think about whether it will be easier to find pairs of corresponding angles that are congruent or pairs of corresponding sides that are congruent. Then, check to see if all the information matches the Angle-Side-Angle, Side-Angle-Side, or Side-Side-Side Triangle Congruence Theorem.

iM KH

Lesson 9 Practice Problems

1. A kite is a quadrilateral which has 2 sides next to each other that are congruent and where the other 2 sides are also congruent. Given kite $WXYZ$, show that at least one of the diagonals of a kite decomposes the kite into 2 congruent triangles.

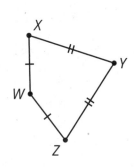

2. Mai has proven that triangle WYZ is congruent to triangle WYX using the Side-Side-Side Triangle Congruence Theorem. Why can she now conclude that diagonal WY bisects angles ZWX and ZYX?

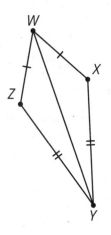

3. $WXYZ$ is a kite. Angle WXY has a measure of 133 degrees and angle ZWX has a measure of 60 degrees. Find the measure of angle ZYW.

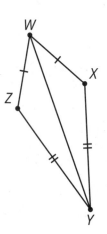

4. Each statement is always true. Select **all** statements for which the converse is also always true.

   A. Statement: If 2 angles form a straight angle, then they are supplementary. Converse: If 2 angles are supplementary, then they form a straight angle.

   B. Statement: In an isosceles triangle, the base angles are congruent. Converse: If the base angles of a triangle are congruent, then the triangle is isosceles.

   C. Statement: If a point is equidistant from the 2 endpoints of a segment, then it lies on the perpendicular bisector of the segment. Converse: If a point lies on the perpendicular bisector of a segment, then it is equidistant from the 2 endpoints of the segment.

   D. Statement: If 2 angles are vertical, then they are congruent. Converse: If 2 angles are congruent, then they are vertical.

   E. Statement: If 2 lines are perpendicular, then they intersect to form 4 right angles. Converse: If 2 lines intersect to form 4 right angles, then they are perpendicular.

(From Unit 2, Lesson 8.)

5. Prove triangle ABD is congruent to triangle CDB.

$DC \parallel AB$

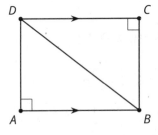

(From Unit 2, Lesson 7.)

iM KH

6. Triangles ACD and BCD are isosceles. Angle DBC has a measure of 84 degrees and angle BDA has a measure of 24 degrees. Find the measure of angle BAC.

$\overline{AD} \cong \overline{AC}$ and $\overline{BD} \cong \overline{BC}$

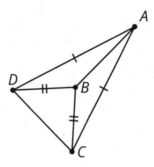

(From Unit 2, Lesson 6.)

7. Reflect right triangle ABC across line AB. Classify triangle CAC' according to its side lengths. Explain how you know.

(From Unit 2, Lesson 1.)

Lesson 10: Practicing Proofs

- Let's practice what we've learned about proofs and congruence.

10.1: Brace Yourself!

What can you do with the braces and fasteners your teacher will give you?

What different ways can you arrange them?

What different quadrilaterals can you make by changing the braces?

Keep track of your findings.

10.2: Card Sort: More Practice Seeing Shortcuts

1. Your teacher will give you a set of cards that show different structures. Sort the cards into 2 categories of your choosing. Be prepared to explain the meaning of your categories. Then, sort the cards into 2 categories in a different way. Be prepared to explain the meaning of your new categories.

2. Sort the cards by rigid vs. flexible structures.

3. State at least one set of triangles that can be proved congruent using:

   a. Side-Angle-Side Triangle Congruence Theorem

   b. Angle-Side-Angle Triangle Congruence Theorem

   c. Side-Side-Side Triangle Congruence Theorem

iM KH

Are you ready for more?

This is the John Hancock Building. What shape do you think surrounds the diagonal braces? List several ways to test your conjecture.

10.3: Matching Pictures to Proofs

Take turns with your partner to match a statement with a diagram that could go with that proof. For each match you find, explain to your partner how you know it's a match. For each match your partner finds, listen carefully to their explanation. If you disagree, discuss your thinking and work to reach an agreement.

1. A quadrilateral with perpendicular diagonals that bisect each other is equilateral.

2. If one diagonal of a quadrilateral is the perpendicular bisector of the other, then 2 pairs of adjacent sides are congruent.

3. Opposite angles in an equilateral quadrilateral are congruent.

4. In a parallelogram, opposite sides are congruent.

Lesson 10 Summary

To prove that segments or angles are congruent, we can look for triangles that those segments or angles are part of. Can the triangles be proven congruent? Are the segments or angles corresponding parts of congruent triangles? Does that help prove the conjecture?

To prove that the triangles are congruent, we can look at the diagram and given information. Think about whether it will be easier to find pairs of corresponding angles that are congruent or pairs of corresponding sides that are congruent. Then check if there's enough information to use the Side-Side-Side, Angle-Side-Angle, or Side-Angle-Side Triangle Congruence Theorems.

Here is an example: Prove that in a quadrilateral with 4 congruent sides, the opposite sides are parallel.

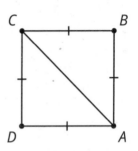

First, sketch a diagram to see what is given and look for congruent triangles. Since this is about a quadrilateral, adding a diagonal to make triangles will be helpful.

Because all the sides of the quadrilateral are congruent, and the triangles formed by the diagonals share a third side, we can use the Side-Side-Side Triangle Congruence Theorem to prove that triangles ABC and CDA are congruent.

iM KH

Lesson 10 Practice Problems

1. Painters and carpenters use scaffolding to climb buildings from the outside. What shapes do you see? Why does one figure have more right angles?

2. Select **all** true statements based on the diagram.

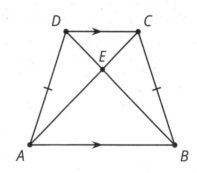

   A. Angle CBE is congruent to angle ABE.

   B. Angle CEB is congruent to angle DEA.

   C. Segment DA is congruent to segment CB.

   D. Segment DC is congruent to segment AB.

   E. Line DC is parallel to line AB.

   F. Line DA is parallel to line CB.

3. Prove $ABCD$ is a parallelogram.

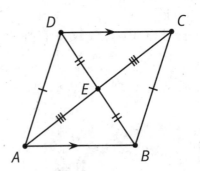

4. Tyler has proven that triangle WYZ is congruent to triangle WYX using the Side-Side-Side Triangle Congruence Theorem. Why can he now conclude that diagonal WY bisects angles ZWX and ZYX?

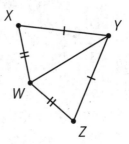

(From Unit 2, Lesson 9.)

5. $WXYZ$ is a kite. Angle WXY has a measure of 133 degrees and angle ZYX has a measure of 34 degrees. Find the measure of angle ZWY.

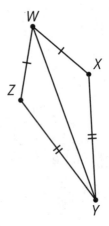

(From Unit 2, Lesson 9.)

6. Elena is thinking through a proof using a reflection to show that the base angles of an isosceles triangle are congruent. Complete the missing information for her proof.

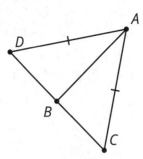

Call the midpoint of segment CD _____1_____ . Construct the perpendicular bisector of segment CD. The perpendicular bisector of CD must go through B since it's the midpoint. A is also on the perpendicular of CD because the distance from A to _____2_____ is the same as the distance from A to _____3_____ . We want to show triangle ADC is congruent to triangle ACD. Reflect triangle ADC across line _____4_____ . Since _____5_____ is on the line of reflection, it definitely lines up with itself. DB is congruent to _____6_____ since AB is the perpendicular bisector of CD. D' will coincide with _____7_____ since it is on the other side of a perpendicular line and the same distance from it (and that's the definition of reflection!). C' will coincide with _____8_____ since it is on the other side of a perpendicular line and the same distance from it (and that's the definition of reflection!). Since the rigid transformation will take triangle ADC onto triangle ACD, that means angle _____9_____ will be taken onto angle _____10_____ (they are corresponding parts under the same reflection), and therefore they are congruent.

(From Unit 2, Lesson 8.)

7. Segment EG is an angle bisector of angle FGH. Noah wrote a proof to show that triangle HEG is congruent to triangle FEG. Noah's proof is not correct. Why is Noah's proof incorrect?

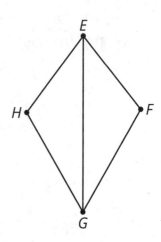

○ Side EG is congruent to side EG because they're the same segment.

○ Angle EGH is congruent to angle EGF because segment EG is an angle bisector of angle FGH.

○ Angle HEG is congruent to angle FEG because segment EG is an angle bisector of angle FGH.

○ By the Angle-Side-Angle Triangle Congruence Theorem, triangle HEG is congruent to triangle FEG.

(From Unit 2, Lesson 7.)

8. Figure $HNMLKEFG$ is the image of figure $ABCDKLMN$ after being rotated 90 degrees counterclockwise around point K. Draw an auxiliary line in figure $ABCDKLMN$ to create a quadrilateral. Draw the image of the auxiliary line when rotated 90 degrees counterclockwise around point K.

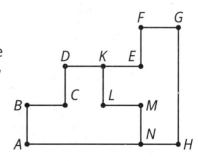

Write a congruence statement for the quadrilateral you created in figure $ABCDKLMN$ and the image of the quadrilateral in figure $HNMLKEFG$.

(From Unit 2, Lesson 2.)

iM KH

Lesson 11: Side-Side-Angle (Sometimes) Congruence

- Let's explore triangle congruence criteria that are ambiguous.

11.1: Notice and Wonder: Congruence Fail

What do you notice? What do you wonder?

In triangles GBD and KHI:

- Angle GBD is congruent to angle KHI.

- Segment BD is congruent to segment HI.

- Segment DG is congruent to segment IK.

11.2: Dare to Be (Even More) Different

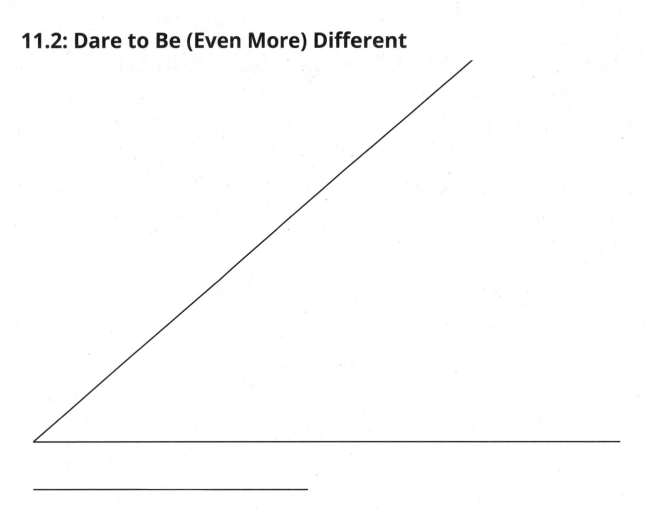

Copy these segments and use them to make a triangle using the given angle so that the given angle is *not* between the 2 given sides. Draw your triangle on tracing paper. Try to make your triangle different from the triangles drawn by the other people in your group.

11.3: Ambiguously Ambiguous?

Your teacher will give you some sets of information.

- For each set of information, make a triangle using that information.

- If you think you can make more than one triangle, make more than one triangle.

- If you think you can't make any triangle, note that.

When you are confident they are accurate, create a visual display.

iM KH

Are you ready for more?

Triangle ABC is shown. Use your straightedge and compass to construct a new point D on line AC so that the length of segment BD is the same as the length of segment BC.

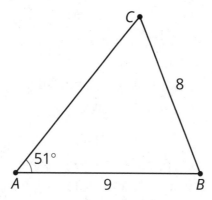

Now use the straightedge and compass to construct the midpoint of CD. Label that midpoint M.

1. Explain why triangle ABM is a right triangle.

2. Explain why knowing the angle at A and the side lengths of AB and BC was not enough to define a unique triangle, but knowing the angle at A and the side lengths of AB and BM would be enough to define a unique triangle.

Lesson 11 Summary

Imagine we know triangles have 2 pairs of corresponding, congruent side lengths, and a pair of corresponding, congruent angles that is not between the given sides. What can we conclude?

Sometimes this is not enough information to determine that the triangles made with those measurements are congruent. These triangles have 2 pairs of congruent sides and a pair of congruent angles, but they are not congruent triangles.

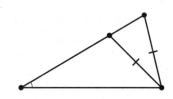

If the longer of the 2 given sides is opposite the given angle though, that does guarantee congruent triangles. In a right triangle, the longest side is always the hypotenuse. If we know the hypotenuse and the leg of a right triangle, we can be confident they are congruent.

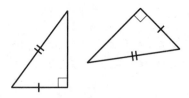

iM KH

Lesson 11 Practice Problems

1. Which of the following criteria *always* proves triangles congruent? Select **all** that apply.

   A. 3 congruent angles

   B. 3 congruent sides

   C. Corresponding congruent Side-Angle-Side

   D. Corresponding congruent Side-Side-Angle

   E. Corresponding congruent Angle-Side-Angle

2. Here are some measurements for triangle ABC and triangle XYZ:

   ○ Angle ABC and angle XYZ are both 30°

   ○ BC and YZ both measure 6 units

   ○ CA and ZX both measure 4 units

   Lin thinks thinks these triangles must be congruent. Priya says she knows they might not be congruent. Construct 2 triangles with the given measurements that aren't congruent. Explain why triangles with 3 congruent parts aren't necessarily congruent.

3. Jada states that diagonal WY bisects angles ZWX and ZYX. Is she correct? Explain your reasoning,

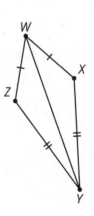

(From Unit 2, Lesson 9.)

4. Select **all** true statements based on the diagram.

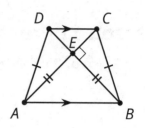

    A. Angle CBE is congruent to angle DAE.

    B. Angle CEB is congruent to angle DEA.

    C. Segment DA is congruent to segment CB.

    D. Segment DC is congruent to segment AB.

    E. Line DC is parallel to line AB.

    F. Line DA is parallel to line CB.

(From Unit 2, Lesson 10.)

5. $WXYZ$ is a kite. Angle WXY has a measure of 94 degrees and angle ZWX has a measure of 112 degrees. Find the measure of angle ZYW.

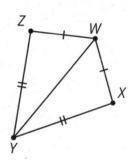

(From Unit 2, Lesson 9.)

iM KH

6. Andre is thinking through a proof using a reflection to show that a triangle is isosceles given that its base angles are congruent. Complete the missing information for his proof.

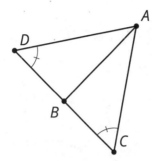

Construct AB such that AB is the perpendicular bisector of segment CD. We know angle ADB is congruent to _____1_____. DB is congruent to _____2_____ since AB is the perpendicular bisector of CD.
Angle _____3_____ is congruent to angle _____4_____ because they are both right angles. Triangle ABC is congruent to triangle _____5_____ because of the _____6_____ Triangle Congruence Theorem. AD is congruent to _____7_____ because they are corresponding parts of congruent triangles. Therefore, triangle ADC is an isosceles triangle.

(From Unit 2, Lesson 8.)

7. The triangles are congruent. Which sequence of rigid motions takes triangle DEF onto triangle BAC?

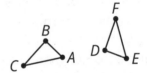

A. Translate DEF using directed line segment EA. Rotate $D'E'F'$ using A as the center so that D' coincides with C. Reflect $D''E''F''$ across line AC.

B. Translate DEF using directed line segment EA. Rotate $D'E'F'$ using A as the center so that D' coincides with C. Reflect $D''E''F''$ across line AB.

C. Translate DEF using directed line segment EA. Rotate $D'E'F'$ using A as the center so that D' coincides with B. Reflect $D''E''F''$ across line AC.

D. Translate DEF using directed line segment EA. Rotate $D'E'F'$ using A as the center so that D' coincides with B. Reflect $D''E''F''$ across line AB.

(From Unit 2, Lesson 3.)

Lesson 12: Proofs about Quadrilaterals

- Let's prove theorems about quadrilaterals and their diagonals.

12.1: Play with Parallelograms

1. Make several parallelograms with your strips.

2. Make several **rectangles** with your strips.

12.2: From Conjecture to Proof

Here are some conjectures:

- All rectangles are parallelograms.

- If a parallelogram has (at least) one right angle, then it is a rectangle.

- If a quadrilateral has 2 pairs of opposite sides that are congruent, then it is a parallelogram.

- If the diagonals of a quadrilateral both bisect each other, then the quadrilateral is a parallelogram.

- If the diagonals of a quadrilateral both bisect each other and they are perpendicular, then the quadrilateral is a **rhombus**.

1. Pick one conjecture and use the strips to convince yourself it is true.

2. Re-write the conjecture to identify the given information and the statement to prove.

iM KH

3. Draw a diagram of the situation. Mark the given information and any information you can figure out for sure.

4. Write a rough draft of how you might prove your conjecture is true.

12.3: Checking a Proof

Exchange proofs with your partner. Read the rough draft of their proof. If it convinces you, write a detailed proof together following their plan. If it does not convince you, suggest changes that will make the proof convincing.

Are you ready for more?

Draw 2 circles (of different sizes) that intersect in 2 places. Label the centers A and B and the points of intersection C and D. Prove that segment AB must be perpendicular to segment CD.

Lesson 12 Summary

Why did we spend so much time learning about when triangles are congruent? Because we can decompose other shapes into triangles. By looking for triangles that must be congruent we can prove other shapes have many properties. For example we could learn more about these types of quadrilaterals:

- A parallelogram is a quadrilateral with both pairs of opposite sides parallel.

- A **rectangle** is a quadrilateral with 4 right angles.

- A **rhombus** is a quadrilateral with 4 congruent sides.

- A square is a quadrilateral with 4 right angles and 4 congruent sides.

- A kite is a quadrilateral which has 2 sides next to each other that are congruent and where the other 2 sides are also congruent.

Knowing how to decompose quadrilaterals into triangles using their diagonals lets us prove how the different quadrilaterals' definitions lead to their diagonals having different properties. We can also look at whether arranging the diagonals to have certain properties gives us enough information to prove which type of quadrilateral must be formed. For example, we might conjecture that if one diagonal is the perpendicular bisector of the other, the figure is a kite. But how do we turn that into a statement that we can prove?

Here is a specific statement that shows what we mean by "one diagonal is the perpendicular bisector of the other" and "the figure is a kite." In quadrilateral $ABCD$ with diagonals AC and BD, the diagonals intersect at P. Segment AP is congruent to segment PC, and AC is perpendicular to BD. Prove that segment AB is congruent to segment BC, and that segment CD is congruent to segment DA. This specific statement lets us draw and label a diagram, which might give us some ideas about how to prove the statement is true.

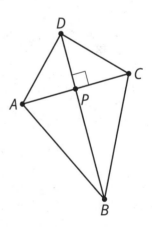

Glossary

- rectangle
- rhombus

Lesson 12 Practice Problems

1. Lin is using the diagram to prove the statement, "If a parallelogram has one right angle, it is a rectangle." Given that *EFGH* is a parallelogram and angle *HEF* is right, which reasoning about angles will help her prove that angle *FGH* is also a right angle?

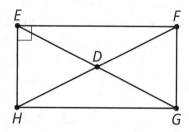

A. Corresponding angles are congruent when parallel lines are cut by a transversal.

B. Opposite angles in a parallelogram are congruent.

C. Vertical angles are congruent.

D. The base angles of an isosceles triangle are congruent.

2. *ABDE* is an isosceles trapezoid. Select **all** pairs of congruent triangles.

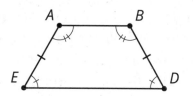

A. Triangle *ABE* and triangle *DBE*

B. Triangle *ABD* and triangle *DAE*

C. Triangle *ABE* and triangle *BAD*

D. Triangle *AED* and triangle *BDE*

E. Triangle *EAB* and triangle *EDB*

3. Match each conjecture with the rephrased statement of proof connected to the diagram.

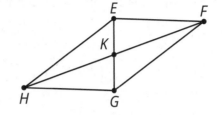

A. The diagonals of a parallelogram bisect each other.

B. In a parallelogram, opposite sides are congruent.

C. A quadrilateral with opposite sides congruent is a parallelogram.

D. If the diagonals of a quadrilateral bisect each other, then it is a parallelogram.

1. In quadrilateral $EFGH$ with GH congruent to FE and EH congruent to FG, show $EFGH$ is a parallelogram.

2. In parallelogram $EFGH$, show GH is congruent to FE and EH congruent to FG.

3. In quadrilateral $EFGH$ with EK congruent to KG and FK congruent to KH, show $EFGH$ is a parallelogram.

4. In parallelogram $EFGH$, show EK is congruent to KG and FK congruent to KH.

4. Which of the following criteria *always* proves triangles congruent? Select **all** that apply.

A. Corresponding congruent Angle-Side-Angle

B. Corresponding congruent Side-Angle-Side

C. Corresponding congruent Side-Side-Angle

D. 3 congruent sides

E. 2 congruent sides

F. 3 congruent angles

(From Unit 2, Lesson 11.)

5. Select **all** true statements based on the diagram.

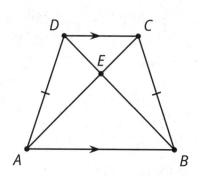

      A. Segment EB is congruent to segment AD.

      B. Segment DC is congruent to segment AB.

      C. Segment DA is congruent to segment CB.

      D. Angle CBE is congruent to angle ABE.

      E. Angle CEB is congruent to angle DEA.

      F. Line DA is parallel to line CB.

      G. Line DC is parallel to line AB.

(From Unit 2, Lesson 10.)

6. Diego states that diagonal WY bisects angles ZWX and ZYX. Is he correct? Explain your reasoning.

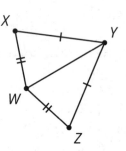

(From Unit 2, Lesson 9.)

7. Sketch the unique triangles that can be made with angle measures 80° and 20° and side length 5. How do you know you have sketched all possibilities?

(From Unit 2, Lesson 4.)

iM KH

Lesson 13: Proofs about Parallelograms

- Let's prove theorems about parallelograms.

13.1: Notice and Wonder: Diagonals

Here is parallelogram $ABCD$ and rectangle $EFGH$. What do you notice? What do you wonder?

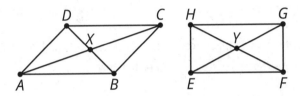

13.2: The Diagonals of a Parallelogram

Conjecture: The diagonals of a parallelogram bisect each other.

1. Use the tools available to convince yourself the conjecture is true.

2. Convince your partner that the conjecture is true for any parallelogram. Can the 2 of you think of different ways to convince each other?

3. What information is needed to prove that the diagonals of a parallelogram bisect each other?

4. Prove that segment AC bisects segment BD, and that segment BD bisects segment AC.

13.3: Work Backwards to Prove

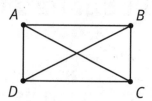

Given: $ABCD$ is a parallelogram with AB parallel to CD and AD parallel to BC. Diagonal AC is congruent to diagonal BD.

Prove: $ABCD$ is a rectangle (angles $A, B, C,$ and D are right angles).

With your partner, you will work backwards from the statement to the proof until you feel confident that you can prove that $ABCD$ is a rectangle using only the given information.

Start with this sentence: I would know $ABCD$ is a rectangle if I knew _____.
Then take turns saying this sentence: I would know [what my partner just said] if I knew _____.

Write down what you each say. If you get to a statement and get stuck, go back to an earlier statement and try to take a different path.

iM KH

Are you ready for more?

Two intersecting segments always make a quadrilateral if you connect the endpoints. What has to be true about the intersecting segments in order to make a(n):

1. rectangle

2. rhombus

3. square

4. kite

5. isosceles trapezoid

Lesson 13 Summary

A quadrilateral is a parallelogram if and only if its diagonals bisect each other. The "if and only if" language means that both the statement and its *converse* are true. So we need to prove:

1. If a quadrilateral has diagonals that bisect each other, then it is a parallelogram.

2. If a quadrilateral is a parallelogram, then its diagonals bisect each other.

To prove part 1, make the statement specific: If quadrilateral $EFGH$ with diagonals EG and FH intersecting at Y so that EY is congruent to YG and FY is congruent to YH, then side EF is parallel to side GH and side EH is parallel to side FG.

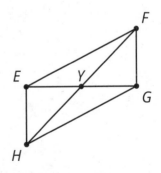

We could prove triangles EYH and GYF are congruent by the Side-Angle-Side Triangle Congruence Theorem. That means that corresponding angles in the triangles are congruent, so angle YEH is congruent to YGF. This means that alternate interior angles formed by lines EH and FG are congruent, so lines EH and FG are parallel. We could also make an argument that shows triangles EYF and GYH are congruent, so that angles FEY and HGY are congruent, which means that lines EF and GH must be parallel.

To prove part 2, make the statement specific: If parallelogram $ABCD$ has side AB parallel to side CD and side AD parallel to side BC, and diagonals AC and BD that intersect at X, then we are trying to prove that X is the midpoint of AC and of BD.

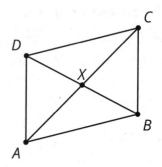

We could use a transformation proof. Rotate parallelogram $ABCD$ by 180° using the midpoint of diagonal AC as the center of the rotation. Then show that the midpoint of diagonal AC is also the midpoint of diagonal BD. That point must be X since it is the only point on both line AC and line BD. So X must be the midpoints of both diagonals, meaning the diagonals bisect each other.

We have proved that any quadrilateral with diagonals that bisect each other is a parallelogram, and that any parallelogram has diagonals that bisect each other. Therefore, a quadrilateral is a parallelogram *if and only if* its diagonals bisect each other.

Lesson 13 Practice Problems

1. Conjecture: A quadrilateral with one pair of sides both congruent and parallel is a parallelogram.

    a. Draw a diagram of the situation.

    b. Mark the given information.

    c. Restate the conjecture as a specific statement using the diagram.

2. In quadrilateral $ABCD$, AD is congruent to BC, and AD is parallel to BC. Show that $ABCD$ is a parallelogram.

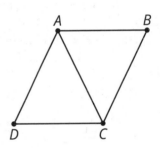

3. $ABDE$ is an isosceles trapezoid. Name one pair of congruent triangles that could be used to show that the diagonals of an isosceles trapezoid are congruent.

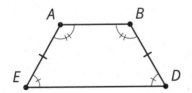

(From Unit 2, Lesson 12.)

4. Select the conjecture with the rephrased statement of proof to show the diagonals of a parallelogram bisect each other.

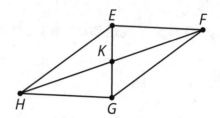

A. In parallelogram $EFGH$, show triangle HEF is congruent to triangle FGH.

B. In parallelogram $EFGH$, show triangle EKH is congruent to triangle GKF.

C. In parallelogram $EFGH$, show EK is congruent to KG and FK is congruent to KH.

D. In quadrilateral $EFGH$ with GH congruent to FE and EH congruent to FG, show $EFGH$ is a parallelogram.

(From Unit 2, Lesson 12.)

5. Is triangle EJH congruent to triangle EIH? Explain your reasoning.

$$\overline{HJ} \perp \overline{JE}, \overline{HI} \perp \overline{IE}, \overline{HJ} \cong \overline{HI}$$

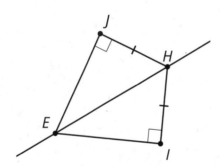

(From Unit 2, Lesson 11.)

iM KH

6. Select **all** true statements based on the diagram.

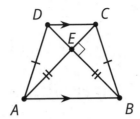

A. Segment DC is congruent to segment AB.

B. Segment DA is congruent to segment CB.

C. Line DC is parallel to line AB.

D. Line DA is parallel to line CB.

E. Angle CBE is congruent to angle DEA.

F. Angle CEB is congruent to angle DEA.

(From Unit 2, Lesson 10.)

7. Which conjecture is possible to prove?

A. If the four angles in a quadrilateral are congruent to the four angles in another quadrilateral, then the two quadrilaterals are congruent.

B. If the four sides in a quadrilateral are congruent to the four sides in another quadrilateral, then the two quadrilaterals are congruent.

C. If the three angles in a triangle are congruent to the three angles in another triangle, then the two triangles are congruent.

D. If the three sides in a triangle are congruent to the three sides in another triangle, then the two triangles are congruent.

(From Unit 2, Lesson 5.)

Lesson 14: Bisect It

- Let's prove that some constructions we conjectured about really work.

14.1: Why Does This Construction Work?

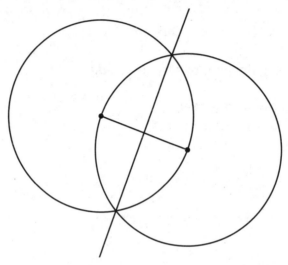

If you are Partner A, explain to your partner what steps were taken to construct the perpendicular bisector in this image.

If you are Partner B, listen to your partner's explanation, and then explain to your partner why these steps produce a line with the properties of a perpendicular bisector.

Then, work together to make sure the main steps in Partner A's explanation have a reason from Partner B's explanation.

iM KH

14.2: Construction from Definition

Han, Clare, and Andre thought of a way to construct an angle bisector. They used a circle to construct points D and E the same distance from A. Then they connected D and E and found the midpoint of segment DE. They thought that ray AF would be the bisector of angle DAE. Mark the given information on the diagram:

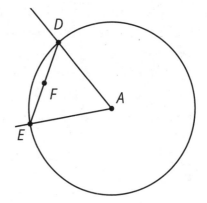

Han's rough-draft justification: F is the midpoint of segment DE. I noticed that F is also on the perpendicular bisector of angle DAE.

Clare's rough-draft justification: Since segment DA is congruent to segment EA, triangle DEA is isosceles. DF has to be congruent to EF because they are the same length. So, AF has to be the angle bisector.

Andre's rough-draft justification: What if you draw a segment from F to A? Segments DF and EF are congruent. Also, angle DAF is congruent to angle EAF. Then both triangles are congruent on either side of the angle bisector line.

1. Each student tried to justify why their construction worked. With your partner, discuss each student's approach.
   - What do you notice that this student understands about the problem?

   - What question would you ask them to help them move forward?

2. Using the ideas you heard and the ways that each student could make their explanation better, write your own explanation for why ray AF must be an angle bisector.

14.3: Reflecting on Reflection

1. Here is a diagram of an isosceles triangle *APB* with segment *AP* congruent to segment *BP*.
   Here is a valid proof that the angle bisector of the vertex angle of an isosceles triangle is a line of symmetry.

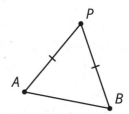

   a. Read the proof and annotate the diagram with each piece of information in the proof.

   b. Write a summary of how this proof shows the angle bisector of the vertex angle of an isosceles triangle is a line of symmetry.

   ○ Segment *AP* is congruent to segment *BP* because triangle *APB* is isosceles.

   ○ The angle bisector of *APB* intersects segment *AB*. Call that point *Q*.

   ○ By the definition of angle bisector, angles *APQ* and *BPQ* are congruent.

   ○ Segment *PQ* is congruent to itself.

   ○ By the Side-Angle-Side Triangle Congruence Theorem, triangle *APQ* must be congruent to triangle *BPQ*.

   ○ Therefore the corresponding segments *AQ* and *BQ* are congruent and corresponding angles *AQP* and *BQP* are congruent.

   ○ Since angles *AQP* and *BQP* are both congruent and supplementary angles, each angle must be a right angle.

   ○ So *PQ* must be the perpendicular bisector of segment *AB*.

   ○ Because reflection across perpendicular bisectors takes segments onto themselves and swaps the endpoints, when we reflect the triangle across *PQ* the vertex *P* will stay in the same spot and the 2 endpoints of the base, *A* and *B*, will switch places.

   ○ Therefore the angle bisector *PQ* is a line of symmetry for triangle *APB*.

iM KH

2. Here is a diagram of parallelogram
   ABCD.
   Here is an invalid proof that a diagonal of
   a parallelogram is a line of symmetry.

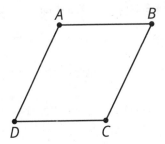

   a. Read the proof and annotate the diagram with each piece of information in the
      proof.

   b. Find the errors that make this proof invalid. Highlight any lines that have errors
      or false assumptions.

   ○ The diagonals of a parallelogram intersect. Call that point M.

   ○ The diagonals of a parallelogram bisect each other, so MB is congruent to MD.

   ○ By the definition of parallelogram, the opposite sides AB and CD are parallel.

   ○ Angles ABM and ADM are alternate interior angles of parallel lines so they
     must be congruent.

   ○ Segment AM is congruent to itself.

   ○ By the Side-Angle-Side Triangle Congruence Theorem, triangle ABM is
     congruent to triangle ADM.

   ○ Therefore the corresponding angles AMB and AMD are congruent.

   ○ Since angles AMB and AMD are both congruent and supplementary angles,
     each angle must be a right angle.

   ○ So AC must be the perpendicular bisector of segment BD.

   ○ Because reflection across perpendicular bisectors takes segments onto
     themselves and swaps the endpoints, when we reflect the parallelogram across
     AC the vertices A and C will stay in the same spot and the 2 endpoints of the
     other diagonal, B and D, will switch places.

   ○ Therefore diagonal AC is a line of symmetry for parallelogram $ABCD$.

Are you ready for more?

There are quadrilaterals for which the diagonals are lines of symmetry.

1. What is an example of such a quadrilateral?

2. How would you modify this proof to be a valid proof for that type of quadrilateral?

Lesson 14 Summary

Earlier we constructed an angle bisector, but we did not prove that the construction always works. Now that we know more we can see why each step is necessary for the construction to precisely bisect an angle. The proof uses some ideas from constructions:

- The midpoint of a segment divides the segment into 2 congruent segments.

- All the radii of a given circle are congruent.

But it also uses some ideas from triangle congruence:

- If triangles have 2 pairs of sides and the angle between them congruent, then the triangles are congruent.

- If triangles are congruent, then the corresponding parts of those triangles are also congruent.

Triangle congruence theorems and properties of rigid transformations can be useful for proving many things, including constructions.

Lesson 14 Practice Problems

1. Select **all** quadrilaterals for which a diagonal is also a line of symmetry.

    A. trapezoid

    B. isosceles trapezoid

    C. parallelogram

    D. rhombus

    E. rectangle

    F. square

2. Show that diagonal EG is a line of symmetry for rhombus $EFGH$.

3. $ABDE$ is an isosceles trapezoid. Priya makes a claim that triangle AEB is congruent to triangle DBE. Convince Priya this is not true.

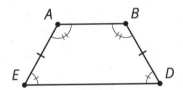

(From Unit 2, Lesson 13.)

4. In quadrilateral $ABCD$, triangle ADC is congruent to CBA. Show that $ABCD$ is a parallelogram.

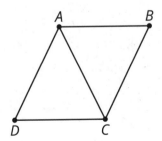

(From Unit 2, Lesson 13.)

5. Priya is convinced the diagonals of the isosceles trapezoid are congruent. She knows that if she can prove triangles congruent that include the diagonals, then she will show that diagonals are also congruent. Help her complete the proof.

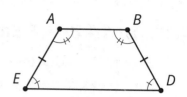

ABDE is an isosceles trapezoid.

Draw auxiliary lines that are diagonals _____1_____ and _____2_____. *AB* is congruent to _____3_____ because they are the same segment. We know angle *B* and _____4_____ are congruent. We know *AE* is congruent to _____5_____. Therefore, triangle *ABE* and _____6_____ are congruent because of _____7_____. Finally, diagonal *BE* is congruent to _____8_____ because _____9_____.

(From Unit 2, Lesson 12.)

6. Is triangle *AFE* congruent to triangle *ADE*? Explain your reasoning.

$$\overline{AF} \cong \overline{AD}, \angle F \cong \angle D$$

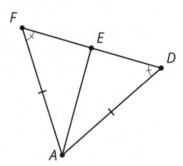

(From Unit 2, Lesson 11.)

7. Triangle *DAC* is isosceles with congruent sides *AD* and *AC*. Which additional given information is sufficient for showing that triangle *DBC* is isosceles? Select **all** that apply.

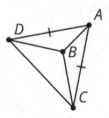

iM KH

A. Segment DB is congruent to segment BC.

B. Segment AB is congruent to segment BD.

C. Angle ABD is congruent to angle ABC.

D. Angle ADC is congruent to angle ACD.

E. AB is an angle bisector of DAC.

F. Triangle BDA is congruent to triangle BDC.

(From Unit 2, Lesson 6.)

Lesson 15: Congruence for Quadrilaterals

- Let's investigate how congruence for quadrilaterals is similar to and different from congruence for triangles.

15.1: True or . . . Sometimes True?: Parallelograms

Given that $ABCD$ is a parallelogram.

1. What must be true?

2. What could possibly be true?

3. What definitely can't be true?

15.2: Floppy Quadrilaterals

Jada is learning about the triangle congruence theorems: Side-Side-Side, Angle-Side-Angle, and Side-Angle-Side. She wonders if there are any theorems like these for parallelograms.

1. If 2 parallelograms have all 4 pairs of corresponding sides congruent, do the parallelograms have to be congruent? If so, explain your reasoning. If not, use the tools available to show that it doesn't work.

iM KH

2. In parallelograms $ABCD$ and $EFGH$, segment AB is congruent to segment EF, segment BC is congruent to segment FG, and angle ABC is congruent to angle EFG. Are $ABCD$ and $EFGH$ congruent? If so, explain your reasoning. If not, use the tools available to show that it doesn't work.

15.3: Make Your Own Congruence Theorem

Come up with another criteria that is enough to be sure that 2 parallelograms are congruent. Try to use as few measurements as you can. Be prepared to convince others that your shortcut works.

Are you ready for more?

1. Will your rule work for any quadrilateral, not just parallelograms?

2. If it does, justify your rule. If it doesn't, adjust your rule so it works for any quadrilateral and justify your new rule.

Lesson 15 Practice Problems

1. Select **all** quadrilaterals that have 180 degree rotational symmetry.

   A. trapezoid

   B. isosceles trapezoid

   C. parallelogram

   D. rhombus

   E. rectangle

   F. square

   (From Unit 2, Lesson 14.)

2. Lin wrote a proof to show that diagonal *EG* is a line of symmetry for rhombus *EFGH*. Fill in the blanks to complete her proof.

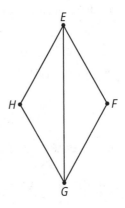

Because *EFGH* is a rhombus, the distance from *E* to _____1_____ is the same as the distance from *E* to _____2_____. Since *E* is the same distance from _____3_____ as it is from _____4_____, it must lie on the perpendicular bisector of segment _____5_____. By the same reasoning, *G* must lie on the perpendicular bisector of _____6_____. Therefore, line _____7_____ is the perpendicular bisector of segment *FH*. So reflecting rhombus *EFGH* across line _____8_____ will take *E* to _____9_____ and *G* to _____10_____ (because *E* and *G* are on the line of reflection) and *F* to _____11_____ and *H* to _____12_____ (since *FH* is perpendicular to the line of reflection, and *F* and *H* are the same distance from the line of reflection, on opposite sides). Since the image of rhombus *EFGH* reflected across *EG* is rhombus *EHGF* (the same rhombus!), line *EG* must be a line of symmetry for rhombus *EFGH*.

(From Unit 2, Lesson 14.)

3. In quadrilateral $ABCD$, AD is congruent to BC, and AD is parallel to BC. Andre has written a proof to show that $ABCD$ is a parallelogram. Fill in the blanks to complete the proof.

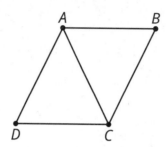

Since AD is parallel to _____1_____, alternate interior angles
_____2_____ and _____3_____ are congruent. AC is congruent to
_____4_____ since segments are congruent to themselves. Along with the given information that AD is congruent to BC, triangle ADC is congruent to
_____5_____ by the _____6_____ Triangle Congruence. Since the triangles are congruent, all pairs of corresponding angles are congruent, so angle DCA is congruent to _____7_____. Since those alternate interior angles are congruent, AB must be parallel to _____8_____. Since we define a parallelogram as a quadrilateral with both pairs of opposite sides parallel, $ABCD$ is a parallelogram.

(From Unit 2, Lesson 13.)

4. Select the statement that **must** be true.

    A. Parallelograms have at least one right angle.

    B. If a quadrilateral has opposite sides that are both congruent and parallel, then it is a parallelogram.

    C. Parallelograms have congruent diagonals.

    D. The height of a parallelogram is greater than the lengths of the sides.

(From Unit 2, Lesson 13.)

iM KH

5. *EFGH* is a parallelogram and angle
   HEF is a right angle.
   Select **all** statements that **must** be true.

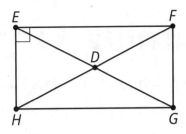

    A. *EFGH* is a rectangle.

    B. Triangle *HEF* is congruent to triangle *GFH*.

    C. Triangle *HEF* is congruent to triangle *FGH*.

    D. *ED* is congruent to *HD*, *DG*, and *DF*.

    E. Triangle *EDH* is congruent to triangle *HDG*.

(From Unit 2, Lesson 12.)

6. Figure *ABCD* is a parallelogram. Is triangle *ADB* congruent to triangle *CBD*? Show
   or explain your reasoning.

$\overline{AB} \cong \overline{CD}, \angle ADB \cong \angle CBD$

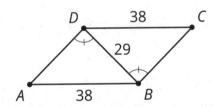

(From Unit 2, Lesson 11.)

7. Figure *KLMN* is a parallelogram. Prove that triangle *KNL* is congruent to
   triangle *MLN*.

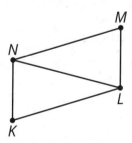

(From Unit 2, Lesson 7.)

Learning Targets

Lesson 1: Congruent Parts, Part 1

- I can identify corresponding parts from a congruence statement.

- I can use rigid transformations to figure out if figures are congruent.

- I can write a congruence statement.

Lesson 2: Congruent Parts, Part 2

- I can identify corresponding parts from a congruence statement.

- I can use rigid transformations to explain why figures are congruent.

- I can write a congruence statement.

Lesson 3: Congruent Triangles, Part 1

- I can explain why if all the corresponding sides and angles of two triangles are congruent, then the triangles are congruent.

Lesson 4: Congruent Triangles, Part 2

- I can write conjectures about what I need to know to prove two triangles are congruent.

Lesson 5: Points, Segments, and Zigzags

- I can write a proof that segments of the same length are congruent.

Lesson 6: Side-Angle-Side Triangle Congruence

- I can explain why the Side-Angle-Side Triangle Congruence Theorem works.

- I can use the Side-Angle-Side Triangle Congruence Theorem in a proof.

Lesson 7: Angle-Side-Angle Triangle Congruence

- I can explain why the Angle-Side-Angle Triangle Congruence Theorem works.

- I can use the Angle-Side-Angle Triangle Congruence Theorem in a proof.

iM KH

Lesson 8: The Perpendicular Bisector Theorem

- I can critique an explanation of the Perpendicular Bisector Theorem.

- I can explain why the Perpendicular Bisector Theorem is true.

Lesson 9: Side-Side-Side Triangle Congruence

- I can explain why the Side-Side-Side Triangle Congruence Theorem works.

- I can use the Side-Side-Side Triangle Congruence Theorem in a proof.

Lesson 10: Practicing Proofs

- I can use the Side-Side-Side, Angle-Side-Angle, and Side-Angle-Side Triangle Congruence Theorems in proofs.

- I can write conjectures about quadrilaterals.

Lesson 11: Side-Side-Angle (Sometimes) Congruence

- I know Side-Side-Angle does not guarantee triangles are congruent.

Lesson 12: Proofs about Quadrilaterals

- I can critique a proof about quadrilaterals.

- I can prove theorems about quadrilaterals.

- I can rewrite a conjecture so it is specific enough to prove.

Lesson 13: Proofs about Parallelograms

- I can prove theorems about the diagonals of a parallelogram.

Lesson 14: Bisect It

- I can critique a proof about constructions.

- I can explain why constructions work.

Lesson 15: Congruence for Quadrilaterals

- I can use rigid transformations to prove quadrilaterals are congruent.

- I can write conjectures about quadrilateral congruence.

Glossary

angle bisector

A line through the vertex of an angle that divides it into two equal angles.

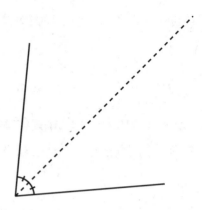

assertion

A statement that you think is true but have not yet proved.

auxiliary line

An extra line drawn in a figure to reveal hidden structure.

For example, the line shown in the isosceles triangle is a line of symmetry, and the lines shown in the parallelogram suggest a way of rearranging it into a rectangle.

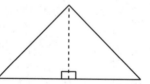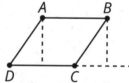

circle

A circle of radius r with center O is the set of all points that are a distance r units from O.

To draw a circle of radius 3 and center O, use a compass to draw all the points at a distance 3 from O.

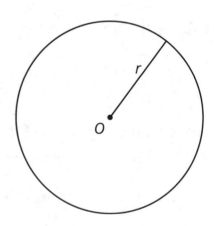

iM KH

congruent

One figure is called congruent to another figure if there is a sequence of translations, rotations, and reflections that takes the first figure onto the second.

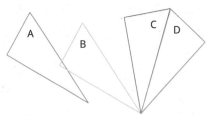

conjecture

A reasonable guess that you are trying to either prove or disprove.

converse

The converse of an if-then statement is the statement that interchanges the hypothesis and the conclusion. For example, the converse of "if it's Tuesday, then this must be Belgium" is "if this is Belgium, then it must be Tuesday."

corresponding

For a rigid transformation that takes one figure onto another, a part of the first figure and its image in the second figure are called corresponding parts. We also talk about corresponding parts when we are trying to prove two figures are congruent and set up a correspondence between the parts to see if the parts are congruent.

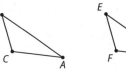

In the figure, segment AB corresponds to segment DE, and angle BCA corresponds to angle EFD.

directed line segment

A line segment with an arrow at one end specifying a direction.

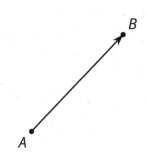

image

If a transformation takes A to A', then A is the original and A' is the image.

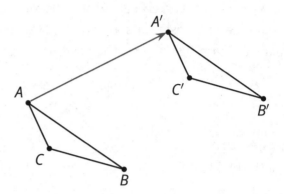

inscribed

We say a polygon is inscribed in a circle if it fits inside the circle and every vertex of the polygon is on the circle. We say a circle is inscribed in a polygon if it fits inside the polygon and every side of the polygon is tangent to the circle.

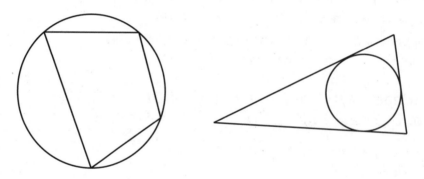

line of symmetry

A line of symmetry for a figure is a line such that reflection across the line takes the figure onto itself.

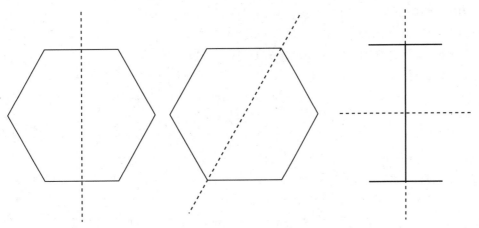

The figure shows two lines of symmetry for a regular hexagon, and two lines of symmetry for the letter I.

line segment
A set of points on a line with two endpoints.

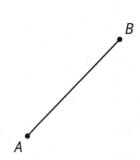

parallel
Two lines that don't intersect are called parallel. We can also call segments parallel if they extend into parallel lines.

parallelogram
A quadrilateral in which pairs of opposite sides are parallel.

perpendicular bisector

The perpendicular bisector of a segment is a line through the midpoint of the segment that is perpendicular to it.

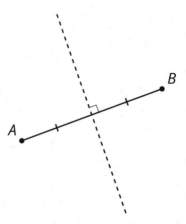

rectangle

A quadrilateral with four right angles.

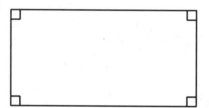

reflection

A reflection is defined using a line. It takes a point to another point that is the same distance from the given line, is on the other side of the given line, and so that the segment from the original point to the image is perpendicular to the given line.

In the figure, A' is the image of A under the reflection across the line m.

Reflect A across line m.

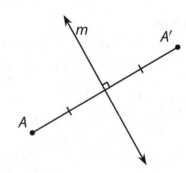

iM KH

reflection symmetry

A figure has reflection symmetry if there is a reflection that takes the figure to itself.

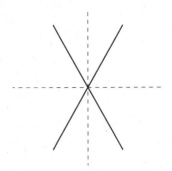

regular polygon

A polygon where all of the sides are congruent and all the angles are congruent.

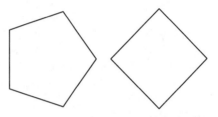

rhombus

A quadrilateral with four congruent sides.

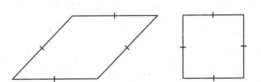

rigid transformation

A rigid transformation is a translation, rotation, or reflection. We sometimes also use the term to refer to a sequence of these.

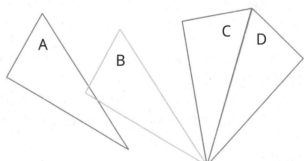

rotation

A rotation has a center and a directed angle. It takes a point to another point on the circle through the original point with the given center. The 2 radii to the original point and the image make the given angle.

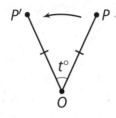

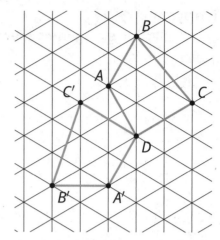

P' is the image of P after a counterclockwise rotation of $t°$ using the point O as the center.

Quadrilateral $ABCD$ is rotated 120 degrees counterclockwise using the point D as the center.

rotation symmetry

A figure has rotation symmetry if there is a rotation that takes the figure onto itself. (We don't count rotations using angles such as 0° and 360° that leave every point on the figure where it is.)

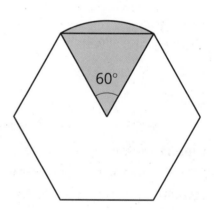

symmetry

A figure has symmetry if there is a rigid transformation which takes it onto itself (not counting a transformation that leaves every point where it is).

tessellation

An arrangement of figures that covers the entire plane without gaps or overlaps.

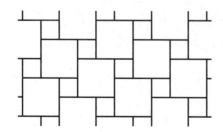

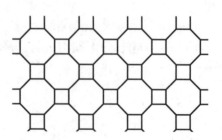

iM KH

theorem

A statement that has been proved mathematically.

translation

A translation is defined using a directed line segment. It takes a point to another point so that the directed line segment from the original point to the image is parallel to the given line segment and has the same length and direction.

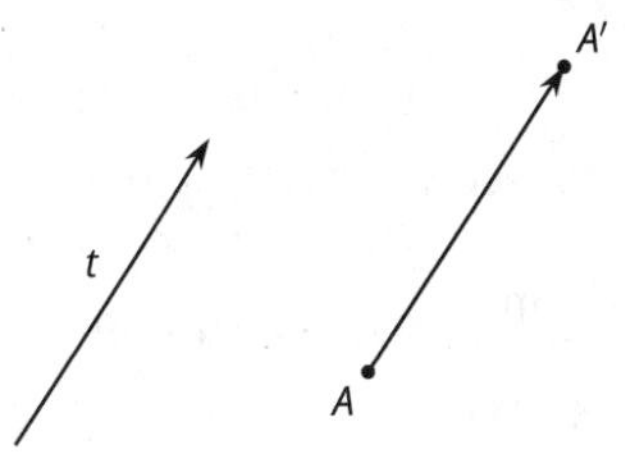

In the figure, A' is the image of A under the translation given by the directed line segment t.

Attributions

"Notice and Wonder" and "I Notice/I Wonder" are trademarks of the National Council of Teachers of Mathematics, reflecting approaches developed by the Math Forum (http://www.nctm.org/mathforum/), and used here with permission.

Images that are not the original work of Illustrative Mathematics are in the public domain or released under a Creative Commons Attribution (CC-BY) license, and include an appropriate citation. Images that are the original work of Illustrative Mathematics do not include such a citation.

Image Attributions

The taichi symbol, by Gregory Maxwell . Public Domain. https://en.wikipedia.org/wiki/Yin_and_yang#/media/File:Yin_yang.svg.

The Saltire, by Unknown. Public Domain. https://simple.wikipedia.org/wiki/Flag_of_Scotland#/media/File:Flag_of_Scotland.svg.

Three Legs of Man, by MartyIOM. Public Domain. https://commons.wikimedia.org/wiki/Triskelion#/media/File:Three_Legs_of_Man_-_Triskelion.jpg.

Kite, by Schoolfreeware. Public Domain. https://openclipart.org/detail/19648/kite.

Back with scaffolding, by Baltimore Heritage. Public Domain. Eli Pousson. https://www.flickr.com/photos/baltimoreheritage/32483635746/.

Nepali style scaffolding (and wires), by Stig Berge. Public Domain. https://www.flickr.com/photos/146415579@N02/39290479945/.

iM KH

Citations

Unit 1: Constructions and Rigid Transformations

Lesson 2

Baroody, J. (2016). Geometry construction project. Retrieved from https://baroody.org/GeometryHonors/Miscellaneous/Construction%20Project.pdf

Lesson 22

Baroody, J. (2016). Geometry construction project. Retrieved from https://baroody.org/GeometryHonors/Miscellaneous/Construction%20Project.pdf

Notes

Notes